o finland

Stories, Poems and Illustrations

by Americans of Finnish Origin

To Cuz from Val.

Edited by:

Judy Harvala Henderson
and
David William Salmela

o finland

Published by:

OTSA PRESS
5871 Covington Lane
Minnetonka, MN 55345-6216

Books may be ordered from the above address.

ISBN No. 0-9649064-2-2

CONTENTS

Mary Kinnunen is founding publisher of Marquette Monthly, a features magazine for the central Upper Peninsula of Michigan. She edited *Red, White & a Paler Shade of Blue--Poems on the Finnish-American Experience.* Her poems and essays have appeared in *Howling Dog, Nerve Bundle Review, North Coast Review, Maxine, Bike Magazine, Chile Pepper Magazine,* and online in *Poetry Magazine.* She lives in Rhinelander, Wisconsin, where she is a city council alderperson.

Before she became its editor, Lynn Maria Laitala won *The Finnish American Reporter's* First Annual Fiction Competition with her story, "Tamarack Autumn." She currently lives on a small farm in Northern Wisconsin where she keeps horses and chickens.

"I was raised by Finnish peasants who were born in the 19th century, and they continue to be the guiding influence of my life."

Oral histories that Lynn has collected since the early 1970's are the raw material for her stories. Three of them, "Timo's Team," "The Big Wedding," and "Winter Trip," appeared in *Sampo: The Magic Mill, A Collection of Finnish-American Writing* from New Rivers Press.

Anna E. Ahlgren believes that her Finnish heritage has been an integral part of her life, from attending Salolampi as a youth to traveling to Finland as one of ten American participants in the Finland-U.S. Senate Scholarship Exchange in 1987.

Ahlgren was the first recipient of the Duncan Award for Excellence in writing while attending the University of Minnesota-Duluth in 1993. A Duluth native, Ahlgren recently moved to the Twin Cities via Yuma, Arizona. She currently teaches Language Arts at a Twin Cities area high school and will participate in the Minnesota Writing Project Selective Institute in the summer of 1998.

David William Salmela is an author of a children's book, *THE SAUNA* and a book of poetry, *KARHUN OTSA*. He is involved with Salolampi, The Finnish Language Village in the summers. He currently lives with his wife, Anne, and two children, Jake and Emily in Minnetonka, Minnesota.

"I enjoy my Finnishness and am pleased to share a portion of it with others who are interested in what it means to be Finnish American."

David has performed his poetry at FinnFest, bookstores, libraries, as well as at various Finnish functions around the Minnesota area. One of his current projects is a collection of poems from each of the saunas he has visited.

Bernice Koehler Johnson has a Master's Degree in Creative Writing and a Certificate in Teaching English as a Second Language. The two disciplines are parallel loves that she exercises by writing about her experiences while teaching English in foreign countries. Resultant stories have appeared in various publications.

"I grew up in northwestern Minnesota near the Finnish community of New York Mills. Although I am only half Finnish, the preponderance of Finns in the area, and my affection for Finnish relatives, convinced me at an early age that I was a true Finn--a designation I still cling to."

Bernice's current projects include compiling collections of family and travel stories.

Sheila J. Packa is the granddaughter of Finnish immigrants. She grew up on the Iron Range and lives in Duluth, Minnesota with her family. She writes fiction and poetry. The story "The Cure" is an excerpt from her novel in progress. Her work has appeared in *Sampo: The Magic Mill, A Collection of Finnish American Writing, North Writers II, Forkroads, Ploughshares,* and several other literary magazines. Poetry Harbor in Duluth recently published her chapbook, *Always Saying Good-bye.*

"I want to stay close to my roots. From the Finnish culture, I've learned to live simply and value the work of the hands. Finns are often independent and ingenious, and invent what they need."

Sheila has received an Arrowhead Arts Council Fellowship Award in 1998, a Loft Mentor Award in poetry in 1993, and two Loft McKnight Awards, one in poetry in 1986 and one in prose in 1996. She received the Poetry Grand Prize in 1995, from *The Finnish American Reporter.* She has an MFA in Creative Writing from Goddard College, Vermont.

Jake presently lives in Maple Plain, Minnesota. In the spring of 1993 Jake married Laurie and her four children, two girls and two boys. At the time the girls were 15 and 13 years old and the boys 7 and 5 years old.

Jake works in the building industry through a wholesale millwork company. While not working, Jake enjoys traveling (particularly Washington state where he lived for nearly seven years).

Jake and Laurie enjoy watching the children grow, as well as their summertime garden.

Also being the youngest of eight children, Jake is an uncle many times and has enjoyed watching his nephews and nieces make their way through life's travels.

Biography on Page 65.

Kirsten (Paurus) Dierking's poetry has been published in numerous journals and anthologies, including *Red, White, and a Paler Shade of Blue*, an anthology of Finnish-American writers distributed at FinnFest 1996.

"I spent a lot of time as a child in my grandparents' Finnish speaking household, and many hours roasting in the sauna with my family on Saturday nights. It was only recently that my relatives discovered my grandmother's Sami heritage. I am just beginning to explore how this nomadic reindeer culture fits in with my contemporary American life."

Kirsten lives in St. Paul, Minnesota with her husband, Patrick. She holds a master's degree in creative writing from Hamline University, Minnesota.

Jeff Eaton teaches writing at Nicolet Area Technical College in Rhinelander, Wisconsin. A past Visiting Scholar at Sichuan Normal University in Chengdu, Sichuan, China, he is involved in the International Education initiative of the Wisconsin Technical College System. A former reporter and editor, his journalism and poetry have appeared over the years in a variety of local, regional, and national publications.

Judy Harvala Henderson graduated from Metro State U. at age 52 with an English degree. She and her husband, Don, are self-employed with a tax preparation business in Edina, Minnesota. They have her three children, his four children and seven grandchildren.

"I have thought of myself as 100% Finn, but I neither write, read, nor speak Finnish. I have not been to Finland. But my Finnish face, a body like my sturdy grandmothers, and a Finnish childhood on a subsistence farm lays claim to my viewpoint.

This book, o finland, is our effort to keep the Finnish-American voice active in our American culture."

Julia Klatt Singer lives with her husband Skip, son Maxwell, and dog Ella in Minneapolis, Minnesota. Ms. Singer is presently a rostered Artist for the Minnesota State Arts Board and COMPAS in their writers and artists in the Schools programs.

"Being one quarter Finn, my grandmother used to say I was Finnish from the knees down, but I suspect it's in my pores and taste for cardamom."

To date, Ms. Singer's writing has appeared in over two dozen publications, including: *100 Words*, *Compost*, *Thema*, and *Women's Words*. In past lives, Ms. Singer has been a teacher, waitress and model.

Will Lahti is a Finlander poet/artist, whose poetry has appeared in *Poetry Motel*, *Poetry Harbor*, *Wormwood Review*, and *The Finnish-American Reporter*. He co-authored *KARHUN OTSA* and has published several chapbooks.

"Finlander is a state of mind. I have been acting as a missionary of culture among the toiskieliset since 1995."

He resides in the West Bank neighborhood of Minneapolis, Minnesota with his dog. He spends his time living and breathing. Currently he's pursuing his career as a pedicab driver.

Illustrations:

Mike Kovarik lives with his two dogs in the Uptown area of Minneapolis, Minnesota. He works in a bicycle/snowboard shop and does freelance graphic art design.

Katrine Keranen was born in New York Mills, Minnesota and is an art teacher in the Sebeka, Minnesota schools.

HOMESPUN BARBIE

Mary Kinnunen

I never wanted a Barbie, but my mother gave me one anyway. It seemed strange because she was a dedicated Ph.D. and her interest in Barbie was out of character. How did Barbie get caught in mother's orbit? I wondered then as I studied my Golden Pocket astronomy book at my little green desk.

She started sewing Barbie new clothes. We lived in the far north, on the shores of Lake Superior, and we had to make many of life's fashion extras ourselves. In the evenings after finishing class preparations, she'd whir away on her Husqvarna, then proudly hand me her offerings: a mink stole (real mink), a red and white checked square-dancing dress, a pink satin (real silk) evening dress with a beaded neckline. A somber dark blue and green house dress, floral pedal-pushers, a burgundy velveteen coat, all were made from bits and pieces of my mother's and elder sister's old clothes.

With teeny needles she knit Barbie a fuzzy white wool chook which was so big it smothered the upper half of Barbie's face, making her look like a hostage, or someone recovering from brain surgery.

That same winter my mother knit me a powder blue ski sweater while she watched episodes of Alfred Hitchcock and Perry Mason. But the arms came out the size of long makkara. So we brought it to the church and put it in the box for Lutheran world relief. Destination: Pakistan.

One day while I was playing in my room, my mother stopped by. "Have you tried on any of her clothes?" I was sorry to tell her, that with the exception of the chook, I hadn't.

A few weeks later she asked again. She had taken time to sew these things, and she had made them with love. Guilt pangs burned in my chest. I felt hot around the ears. But I just couldn't bring myself to do it. It didn't occur to me to request a matching Ski-Doo snowmobile suit and a tip-up fishing line so Barbie could accompany me out on the ice. Or a miniature flying saucer so she, too, could tear down the hill behind Olson Library. Watch out for the big pine, Barbie!

When I lay on my bed and saw Barbie propped up on her wire stand across the room, she reminded me of the sticks of cedar kindling my father and I used for .22 practice up at the farm.

After a comfortable period of time had elapsed since my mother's second request, I quietly secured Barbie and her wardrobe away in a mahogany leather vanity case with a cracked mirror, and banished them to the murky higher reaches of my closet. The only time Barbie entered my world after that was when she appeared in commercials or in a friend's bedroom.

In the meantime I dropped ice fishing, and turned my attention to skiing and tennis, and a boyfriend with whom I spent satisfying hours shooting in the quarry.

One gray winter day when I was in high school, a pal mentioned Barbie. "Got one," I told her.

"Go on," she said.

"It's true. She has red hair pulled back in a ponytail and her bangs are curled." I dug the vanity from under the detritus of my childhood and opened it up. There was Barbie and her hand-stitched wardrobe. The pearl earrings had worked their way out of her elfin ears a bit.

My friend laughed maniacally and yanked the earrings out the rest of the way, then shoved them into Barbie's hardened boobs.

I was taken aback. Strange, I thought, but oddly funny. Years later my friend tells me she's gay; and years later nipple piercing is all the rage.

I have a daughter of my own now. Not long ago, while watching her granddaughter playing in the living room, my mother asked me, "Where is your old Barbie?"

"In the basement," I said. "I'll go get her." I found the case wedged between an old tennis racquet and the huge strawberry red Samsonite my parents had given me for high school graduation. It had been almost two decades since I had last seen Barbie and her ensemble.

The three of us sat on the floor, handling Barbie's clothes with a tenderness monks and scientists must afford the Shroud of Turin. Miraculously, Barbie's boob wounds had healed.

These days, mother's orbit swerves down to Florida for winters of sun, surf, and Spanish lessons. Barbie's back in the basement and my pal is out of the closet.

WOODSMOKE

Lynn Maria Laitala

I was almost born in a log cabin. My mother went into labor with me when she was staying at Ruoho Ranta on the roadless side of Fall Lake. Old Antti had to row her across the lake, where he made a boy drive her to town. She got to the hospital in the nick of time.

When I was little I wanted to live like Antti and the other old Finnish trappers did--in a cabin tucked back from the shoreline with a woodshed full of neatly stacked piles of seasoned wood, mojakka simmering on top of a warm wood-stove in a tidy kitchen, bread baking in the oven.

The vision came back to me one night far from Fall Lake and Ruoho Ranta, as I listened to the noise of the freeway and waited for a husband who wasn't coming home. I saw a cabin, light beckoning from the window. A thin plume of smoke rose toward the twilight sky, promising a warm welcome.

The next day I went home to northern Minnesota. For a while I worked in the library at Vermilion Community College, formerly plain old Ely Junior College, tuition-free for the children of the Iron Range. Their immigrant parents had fought for it, and the mines paid the bill. It had become the "the Canoe Country College," attracting kids from all over the state with its emphasis on conservation technology. Kids came up to Ely who liked to camp, though most of the school year they huddled together in any warm place they could find. The library was full when it was thirty below. Students unlaced their felt-lined boots, stripped off layers of jackets and sweaters, and settled down to read in the comfort of central heating. Most of the men looked alike-- serious, bearded fellows with interests in biology or geology--but there was one who laughed easily, eyes twinkling. His name was Tom.

A student who worked with me began asking about him. Gail was the daughter of an officer at the bank who looked like she would be more at home in New York than Ely. She came to work impeccably coifed and manicured, and she often traveled to Minneapolis to shop for clothes.

I told her what I knew about Tom--that he was a student in forestry from Minneapolis and that he was building a cabin near where I lived. She made sure she was behind the desk whenever he came up to check out books and soon he was walking her to class. Often I'd see them engrossed in conversation in the cafeteria.

Gail let her hair grow out and clipped her unpolished fingernails short. By spring she came to work in blue jeans and flannel shirts. She was buoyant and very lovely. One May afternoon she asked me to drive her home. "I'm living out at Tom's place now," she said.

I saw them often that summer--walking together in the long lingering light of midsummer twilight, picking raspberries by the side of the road, or talking intently together at the Voyageur Saloon.

When she came back to work in the fall, I asked her how her summer had gone.

"We worked on the cabin. It's nearly done," she said. "And we got a lot of stuff out of the garden." She laughed. "A bumper crop of beets, anyway."

In October Gail was dragging into the library late and unkempt. She washed her face in the ladies room before work, and washed her hair there at lunch time. I asked how things were going out at the cabin.

"It's cold," she said. "We just can't keep up with the wood supply."

She came to say good-bye to me one Friday in November.

"I dropped out of school, so I have to give up my work-study grant," she said.

I asked her to come visit me sometime. She said that she would, but she never did.

Tom still came into the library occasionally, but he was sullen and self-absorbed. Late one afternoon Gail stomped in after him, laden with layers of wool and down. Both of them smelled strongly of woodsmoke. Gail had smudges of ash on her cheek. She talked to him in furious whispers, and stomped out again without glancing at the counter where she used to work. Tom stared at his magazine for a long time after she had gone, rose heavily, and left.

The last time I saw them together was a bitter March afternoon. They were parked at the turnoff up our road. As I approached, Gail got out of the car screaming. She slammed the door and began to walk toward town--enraged, defiant, features distorted. Tears streamed through soot.

I stopped to offer her a ride, but she waved me on, eyes unseeing. Gail works at her father's bank now. Her hair is in a new style, her fingernails are manicured, and she wears expensive clothes. She gives me a friendly greeting whenever I drop in, but she doesn't smile.

I didn't see Tom again. There's a chain across his driveway. Smoke no longer rises from his cabin.

ONE OF US?

Anna E. Ahlgren

"Hm. Karhu." A long pause grew. The split-second shot of skis on a commercial had long since faded. The last notes of a clarinet hung in the air. "You don't know what that means."

"I do."

"You don't know what it means. You don't *really*."

"Bear. Karhu means bear."

"OH, you *do* know!"

I nodded, trying to watch the sit-com, now back from commercial.

"You know where they make Karhu skis, don't you?"

"In Finland." I stared at the TV, sighed at missing the last punch line. Canned laughter faded, and now my father focused on the TV. Credits rolled, and I asked for the clicker.

"Phillip Narhinen." My dad paused, mulling over the name. "You know that should have umlauts. It should be *Närhinen*."

"You don't even know him. Maybe that's how he spells it."

"Naaarhineyen," my dad drawls at me. "Then it's wrong. It's *Närhinen*."

I sighed. This was an old argument. Not an argument, really. More of a debate that has lasted too long. At a rate of about two sentences a day, conversations last a long time in my family. Topics resurface for weeks, months even. Outsiders could never follow the slow, disjointed pace of family discussions. My dad rose from the recliner to drop the remote in my lap as he headed out to add wood to the sauna.

My boots squeaked on rigid snow as I ran from my car to the door of the bar. Only thirty steps and my lungs ached from the cold air. The first rush of warm air fogged my glasses solid. I let the wooden screen slam behind me and closed the heavy oak door. Giving up on the frozen white film on my glasses, I found my clouded way to the bar and ordered a Black Dog.

"It's about time your got here, Alaina!" Peter bounded from behind, sloshing the head off my beer. "Sorry. We have THE table on the other side of the band."

The Landing was the classic north woods lakeside dive with the quirks of a college-town folk crowd. Thursdays were steeped in tradition: bluegrass and beer. I maneuvered through mismatched tables to the coveted "fire pit". Not only did this table have a fireplace, it had two barber chairs and a clear view of the band. Peter, Emily and Chris were blessed with a stroke of luck or they had been drinking for hours to snag this, the best table in the house.

Wet foam ringed my frosted mug when I set it on the table. Peeking through the tiny cleared circles melting near my nose, I shrugged off my coat and arched it over the back of my chair. "Forget these things, I know what you all look like anyway." I dropped my glasses in a ringed puddle. On his next spin, Chris abducted my beer.

He smiled an impish response to my protests, "Hey, I should get something for saving you a spot by the fire."

My shoulders, tense from the cold, relaxed into residual shudders. I leaned my chair back to take full advantage of the fire's warm glow.

"How can you be the daughter of the SuperFinn? It's only--what?--thirty below out there?" Peter teased, sipping from a freshly frosted mug and wiping his hand on his bare leg. He wore shorts from hundred degrees to ten below. No temperature seemed to reach his body. "You know what you need? A bubble. You could be like John Travolta in that bubble boy movie. Constant temperatures, no breezes...Maybe NASA can sell you a space suit."

Emily scraped her chair across the floor to my side of the table. "Sign me up for one, too." She scooted back farther, closer to the fire. "I'm still cold and I've been drinking for an hour. It's gotta be fifty below out there!"

"Wimps. All of you," Peter laughed sardonically. "You know the

SuperFinn would be embarrassed," he switched to an exaggerated German accent, "to know that his daughter is not fulfilling her genetic...potential."

Emily's forehead wrinkled. "What are you talking about?"

"Don't tell me you've never heard the SuperFinn stories!" Peter's laughter spread a shower of popcorn bits over the table. "Oh, fill her in, Alaina."

Friends called my family, the SuperFinns. Our stories have earned the title "SuperFinn Stories," a mix between the movie *Fargo* and self-depreciating ethnic humor. It was a status symbol to have taken a Lippunen sauna, especially to have "braved the top bench" with my uncle Raimo while the hot water tank bubbled a Jamaican steel drum beat.

I shut my eyes and shook my head until I was goaded and bribed. Don't get me wrong. I love telling Lippunen stories. A storyteller has to keep up the show, though. Make it seem like a treat. "So I'm driving up to my parents' house. It's a Sunday afternoon, early. About as cold as this." I sip my beer. Chris leaned his chair back, suppressing a laugh. I wiped the froth from my lips with a dramatic flourish (to get a little suspense going).

"Get over yourself!" Chris slammed his chair legs down in mock anger and whined, "just tell the story."

"OK. OK. So anyway, I'm pulling up. It's butt cold outside, and my parents are out in the driveway with the truck doors wide open. My mom's holding an ice pick. Just holding it. And my dad's whistling and tinkering around with that old tractor that he bought when he thought my brothers might actually help him start a logging side business."

Emily interrupted, "That rusted monstrosity in your yard? Wouldn't his hand, like, stick to metal or something if it's way below zero?"

Chris and Peter waved her off and shushed her.

"Well, yeah, but that's not the point. The point is they spend their Sunday afternoons standing in the driveway when it's too cold to touch metal. The truck doors are wide open--not that they're going anywhere--and my dad's got his giant blue down parka on. My mom's holding an ice pick, but I don't see any chipping going on," I chuckled, anticipating the punch line.

"I don't get it." Emily stared at us blankly.

"Just wait!"

"So my parents are standing out in eighty-frikin-below with the truck doors wide open just to get good reception for the Finnish radio show out of Virginia."

Emily paused, her face frozen in a fake open smile. "I still don't get it."

"It's a thirty-degree-below zero excuse to listen to Finnish music! Just to listen. Not even so much as a polka to stay warm."

We shook until Emily stared us into the after-laugh sigh.

"Guess you have to know the Lippunens," Chris sputtered.

"You didn't even tell about how your dad drove the truck around the yard to get the best reception," Peter added.

"Oh, he doesn't have to do that anymore since he's identified 'the spot'. It looks like there's a launch pad in the middle of the driveway where the reception is clear. He's got it outlined with paint and everything. And, let me tell you, that driveway is kept *clear*!"

The story telling drifted to Chris's story about his latest spelunking trip to Texas. Among us cave explorers, his jargon-riddle story slipped easily through our conversation. We recalled our first muddy ventures into the underground drainage culverts that trickled water into the lake.

Chris, distracted, finally snapped a "*what?*" at Emily.

Emily shifted uneasily in her seat and slid her hand along side of her nose. "Don't look now," she murmured, "but there's some creepy Canadian-looking guy over there by the band....Oh, that's subtle!" she chided Chris, who was craning to stare. He yanked his head back and she continued, "He's been staring over here and *writing stuff down*."

I stretched my neck and pretended to watch the guitar player. The bluegrass jam ostensibly rapt our attention as we stole glances at our observer. Chris swung around. "Yep. Definitely Canadian. Check out the tinted glasses."

"I don't know. He looks kind of Russian to me. Look at his mouth. His lips are all shiny and...well, you know." Emily said and gave up her spy-pretense and outright stared. "Definitely Russian. That's vodka he's drinking."

"Whatever. He must come from a country without combs."

"Yeah, you should talk, Chris."

"What?" Chris shot a hand up to his hair, patted it in a careful evaluation.   "It looks fine."

"I guess...if you use your hand for a mirror." I got up and shuffled my fingers through Chris's hair till it stood on end, closed my eyes and patted it, teasing, "Ooooh, now it looks great." I slid my chair back and headed to the bathroom.

The hallway was dimly lit, and muffled noise accompanied me to the bathroom. I jiggled the doorknob, then leaned against the wall and stared at a stretch-print of a sailboat.

"You're Alaina Lippunen, aren't you?" I jerked my head. Our observer, the moist-lipped man who had been taking notes at the corner table, was standing against the wall. I shot a glance at the door, then back at the dim figure to my right. Red neon silhouetted his head, lighting a spray of hair at the back of this head--a bedspot, still, in the evening. Even in the dim light, his lips seemed to be coated with saliva. Yellow-tint glasses magnified his eyes; crow's feet splayed out from deep-set dark eyes pushed thin by high, broad cheekbones.

"You're one-hundred percent Finnish, aren't you?" His voice was deep but quiet; the words spilled out too fast.

I checked the doorknob with false subtlety. A flush eased my tense breathing. "Uh, yah," I answered tersely. I kept staring at the sailboat stretch print, memorizing its orange swath. His breath gurgled softly, wheezing as if he had run up a flight of stairs. I tapped my palms against the wall behind me, my ears strained in anticipation of the screeching twist of the doorknob.

"Tell me something," he said.

I looked at him, my brow twisted.

"Do you feel any...pressure? To marry another Finn?"

Now I really started to wonder. A metallic taste pooled in my mouth--fear.   What did he want from me and where were those questions leading? I slanted my eyebrow and flattened my voice, "Not to speak of," I lied.

"Really." He paused. "You're quite unusual....Do you realize *how* unusual you are?"

I heard the clicks of make-up cases from behind the door, sucked in a shallow breath, turned to look him straight in the face. No malicious intention was written in his face. In fact, he seemed disinterested, detached, the cool gaze of a scientist watching a rat navigate a maze.

"I don't think you do," he added. My eyes rolled involuntarily. First my father. Now a stranger. The significance of this one fact was taking over my life.

The door to the women's room was yanked open. With sidelong glances at the stranger, I brushed past the woman exiting and swung the door shut. I switched the lock and caught my breath. Next door, the men's room door clicked shut. No exchange of footsteps. No voices. It had been empty.

I lingered, slowly washing my hands four times until I heard the men's room door swing open and shut on its rusty hinges. I washed my hands again, then slipped out to my seat at the table, half-sprinting past the men's room. At the table, I related my encounter in the hallway to an open-mouthed audience. I glanced around for the stranger. He was in line at the bar. Emily's suggestion that at least he had an original pick-up line brought a round of laughter to the table.

"Maybe," Chris's eyes held a secret, "but I know what he's really getting at." Chris smiled with secret knowledge. "I actually had a chat with this guy a few weeks back. He's all whacked out on medication. He was going off about his secret--the 'truth' about Finns. He had twenty minutes of schlock on this theory."

I sighed impatiently, waiting for an ethnic joke.

Chris continued. "He says you're aliens. Space-men. All this mystery about your origin can only mean one thing, according to him." He arched an eyebrow, "you're 'not of this world'."

"Ha. Ha. Maybe you shouldn't spend your free time getting drunk with mental patients," I said.

Peter conceded, "You've gotta admit, Alaina, that would explain the SuperFinn's obsession with the homeland...or shall we say 'the mother ship'?"

"Tell us the truth." Chris's eyes bled staged honesty, "Were you behind the Kennedy assassination?" I glared flatly at him.

"Be careful," Peter warned, "laser beams could shoot out of her eyes at any moment!"

"I'm gonna get another beer," I slid my chair back and headed for the bar. From the corner of my eye, I caught a glimpse of the stranger studying my trek to the bar. When I reached the line, I glanced back at my observer. He noted my uncomfortable return of his stare, then nodded back to his writing.

I shifted from foot to foot, constrained by his focused stare. Constricted by his view. I don't need to search for who I am in strange theories. To me, heritage has always meant community. It's the people, not the past. I can't follow those who delve into a dim past for enlightenment. Exploring caves has alerted me to inescapable tunnels that mislead those too quick to trust deceitful cracks of light.

The bartender's voice startled me.

"Yeah. I know what I want." I turned without ordering and headed back to the table.

"You know what I was just thinking?" I asked my friends. "How good it feels to just sweat out the world with a long sauna. I'm heading up to my folks'."

THE URBAN BUTCHER

David William Salmela

David looked around his friend's well-kept yard. Towering white pines lofted green branches into the lowering sky. Near the woods the log sauna held the promise of future warmth. David held his leather jacket closed against the probing fingers of the coming winter wind. The grey, November sky seemed to bounce off the roof of his friend's log home.

The city seemed far away from this place. The nearest town was a mile away, and that wasn't even a town. It was nothing more than a closed co-op store at the intersection of two township roads. The co-op had been set up by some hard-working Finns earlier in the century, but succumbed to abandonment with the advent of the automobile and super food stores.

The door to the house opened. His old motorcycle buddy, Rick, stood sleepily in the doorway. Four children hung on his legs, their wide Finnish eyes stared at the man in their yard.

"Huomenta," David said.

"Hei, city poika," said Rick. He said it like one Finnish word, 'sitipoika.'

"Got any coffee? Or do I have to go over and visit the neighbors?"

Rick rubbed his eyes with one muscled hand. His other hand was draped protectively over a child's shoulder. He smiled a little, "No, come in. We've got coffee."

David stepped into the warm kitchen. "It's kind of cold out."

"Winter's coming. You want sugar?"

"Kiitos, ei. I like mine black." The strong coffee scalded his wind-burned lips. "This is good," David grunted.

Rick looked at him. "What's new down there in the city?"

"Same old stuff," David replied over his cup, "cars, trucks, people, and noise...lots of noise. What's new around here?"

"Rodney's butchering pigs. Are you coming?"

David took a long drink of coffee. He mulled it over. He'd never done such a thing. He usually didn't think much beyond the cellophane wrapped pork chops in aisle ten of the supermarket. What if he got sick? He'd heard some stories from his grandparents about drinking a cup of fresh blood. He didn't think he'd be able to do something like that. They wouldn't still do such ancient rituals in these modern times, would they?

"Well?" Rick asked.

"Uh, okay. Sure. Sure I'll help."

"You finish your coffee while I get dressed."

David stood up and walked to the window. He held his coffee cup in both hands. The four children stared silently at him staring silently out the window.

Rick's red truck rattled on the dirt driveway. They wound through the woods and past old fields. Through breaks in the trees the city boy glimpsed bare fields, broken fences, and patches of dark sky. The entire countryside suddenly seemed surrounded by death: sullen skies, bare autumn trees, dead fields, abandoned houses, and soon he'd be killing pigs.

Rick's voice broke in on his thoughts. "How was your drive up?"

"Good," David said. "I left early, way before the morning traffic, way before daytime even. The sky was so overcast I wasn't even sure when morning arrived. I needed my lights the whole trip."

"Well, winter's coming." Rick glanced at David. "It's a good day for butchering.

"Why is that?"

"It's not too hot."

They turned into Rodney's driveway. A cluster of trucks were parked in the yard. The house stood on one side of the road, the barn on the other side. One side of the barn formed one wall of the fenced pig pen. "How many pigs to butcher?" asked David, glancing at all the cars in the yard.

"Three."

"Only three? Why so many people?"

"The work goes faster." They parked and greeted everyone as they got out of the truck. The air smelled cold. David saw some familiar faces.

"Hei, sitipoika!" came shouted greetings.

"Päivää," he countered. David saw men standing around the yard. Some of them leaned on the fence, others held coffee. Children ran here and there. Through the kitchen window he saw someone wave to them. They raised their hands in greeting.

A voice spoke up beside them. "Hei, sitipoika, are you sure you can work in those shoes?" It was Rick's older brother.

David looked down at his hightop sneakers. Everyone else had on workboots or overshoes capable of stepping cleanly through the muddy pig pen. "I thought maybe we'd have a foot race after. I wanted to be ready."

Rick's brother laughed. Then he pointed down the road. "Here comes Dick with the tractor." Everyone turned to look. Dick drove over the hardening ruts in the driveway. The bucket on the front end rattled over every bump. The noise of the exhaust bracketed the group. The tractor rolled into the yard, powered down, and stopped. Dick's cheeks flamed from the cold. He swiped at his runny nose.

He looked to Rodney, "Where do you want it?" he asked.

"Over there," indicated Rodney by tilting his head, "behind the pen. We'll carry them over and hoist them up there."

"Okay," said Dick. He turned toward David. "Sitipoika, kuinka kaupunki on?"

"Hyvää on," David replied.

Dick grinned. He throttled up, engaged the clutch of the tractor and rattled off around to the far side of the pen. Dark clods of mud flew up from the ribs of the huge rear tractor wheels. They hung suspended for a moment against the grey sky before dropping randomly to earth.

The clanking of the metal parts on the tractor made the pigs squeal nervously. David looked at them. They ran snuffling along the wooden rails of the fenceline. When they snorted, puffs of exhaled breath vaporized in the cold air. He wondered if they knew what was going to happen, wondered what last thoughts were rooting around inside their pig brains.

The pigs seemed on edge, pacing quickly in one direction and then in another. But then again, what did he know about the normal behavior of pigs? He was a city boy with minimal rural exposure, especially when it came to butchering.

The activity level in the yard increased. The intensity built. Coffee cups were drained. The leftover brackish liquid was flung to the wind and the cups set down. Knives were unsheathed. Children were told, "Settle down now." Men began moving in different directions.

Some of them walked to the skinning area, others moved to the fence. One man came out of the barn rattling some oats in a metal bucket. The pigs milled around, their snouts quivered at the scent of oats.

Rodney strode out of the house. He held a pistol in one hand and a box of shells in the other. As if on cue, the children grew quiet. The man carrying the bucket opened the gate for Rodney. They both stepped inside, stumbling slightly on the churned mud hardening under the brittle wind. Rodney loaded the gun. He set the box of ammunition on the gatepost. He held out his hand for the bucket of oats.

A cold wind wrapped around David's heart. The tractor chugged expectantly in the background. The sharp clank of a chain on metal made the pigs jump and turn in unison. Rick's brother was attaching the spreader bar to the front end of the tractor. The spreaders held the hind legs of the pigs apart for butchering. It also gave the butchers something to attach a chain on to hoist the pigs aloft.

Rodney clucked his tongue and rattled the oats in the bucket. He held the gun loosely in his free hand. One pig snorted loudly. It immediately trotted over to feed on the offered food. It lowered its head to eat.

The gun barked. Rodney's arm bucked. The report echoed around the outbuildings. The pig dropped. Grain dribbled from its mouth, seeding the frozen November mud. Its dead body twitched spasmodically. A puukko appeared in a chapped hand. The pig's throat was cut with deep hacking thrusts.

Four men quickly carried the pig, its head hanging down, to the spreader bar which was now hitched to the front end loader on the tractor.

The tractor roared to life. Two hooks hung from the spreader bar. The men hung the pig by its rear knuckles on the hooks. "Okay!" someone shouted to Dick, "Haul it up!" The dead pig ascended skyward, but stopped far short of heaven. A puukko sliced the underside of the pig. The neck wound gaped hideously. Blood dripped on the ground in a slow, steady stream. It spattered around each time the carcass was bumped.

Voices muttered. Curt directions were given even though everyone knew what to do. Efficiently, the genitals were removed, the ribcage sawed through, and the bowels extracted. "Okay, gut it out. Careful now, don't break the piss sack."

"Carry those guts over there so we don't slip."

"As soon as I'm done cutting through the brisket and get the head off, you guys start skinning."

A large meat saw severed the final tendons and the spinal cord from the carcass. The saw wielder carried the pig's head several meters away and placed it face up on the ground. Glassy eyes stared up at the deadened sky. Its pink tongue hung stiffly out of its mouth, one oat grain frozen to the pink tip. It seemed like an obscene visual joke. What was once a living animal became a piece of farmer's art. Only David seemed to notice.

"Here sitipoika, your turn."

David turned away from the sight. He accepted the butt end of a sharp puukko. "What do I do?"

"Start peeling the hide. Work from the hind legs downward."

David swallowed. He moved forward. Four of them worked shoulder to shoulder, two on each hind leg of the pig. "Now don't damage the meat, sitipoika. Cut only the hide."

He did as he was bid. He cut into once living flesh...cutting, peeling back, pulling the skin, cutting some more. He worked hard to keep up with the more experienced butchers. Cold wind sliced at his hands as he sliced pig flesh with the keen steel blade.

Once the pig was skinned he was amazed at the transformation of a living animal into hunks of meat. The body seemed designed for butchering. The pig's haunch separated cleanly from the carcass. A space in the tendons formed a ready-made hole to slip in the point of a meathook. Each chunk of meat was easily portable by one person. In no time the meat was hanging in the rafters of the lean-to shed on the side of the barn. Milk crates were stacked one and two high so the men could step up to hang their meat high on the rafters.

"Okay, Rodney, we're ready for another one," shouted Rick.

Rodney walked back to the pen. He rattled the oats in the bucket. The biggest pig only eyed him warily, a glimmer of intelligence in its eyes. The other smaller pig stepped gingerly forward. Its head was erect and snout extended as if trying to smell past the death to the nutrition of the oats. Couldn't it remember the companion that was just slaughtered?

Rodney clucked his tongue reassuringly. The pig took a dainty step forward, lowered its head to eat the oats and **BLAM**! the pig took a step back in surprise. A long squeal was torn away by the wind. The pig sat back on its haunches then toppled slowly to one side. The squeal was replaced by a sickening gurgle.

In a moment the throat was slit and it was hanging upside down in front of the skinners.

"Don't you save the blood?" David asked.

"Ei. There's not enough blood in a pig. Dick's father-in-law is the only one left who makes blood pancakes and blood makkara, but only from cow's blood and he ain't even here anyway," said one of the men.

This time David worked more confidently. Ten minutes later the severed head joined its cousin face up on the ground. David imagined them slowly sinking into the earth. They reminded him of Joukahainen who was sung into the earth by Vanha Väinämöinen, the Kalevala folkhero. Perhaps David was Väinämöinen and the pigs represented Joukahainen. David was the greater poet this day. The pigs didn't stand a chance.

One oat grain was still on the first pig's tongue. The second pig's ears had flopped over, glazed eyes reflected the rolling sky.

"Sitipoika, let's take a break. You want some nuuska?"

"I don't usually chew, but then again, I don't usually slaughter pigs either." He took a pinch from the proffered round tin. The tobacco's bite was bracing. Someone brought strong coffee all around. David tried not to swallow tobacco juice along with the coffee. He sat down on a milk crate.

Rick clapped him on the shoulder. "Having a good time, sitipoika?"

David spat. "Joo, but I know I don't want a ham sandwich for supper."

Rick grinned. "No bacon for breakfast either, I'll bet. Here," he held out a ham hock, "take this. Hang this on the rafter."

David set his coffee on the cold ground. Coffee steam whisked past the snouts of the two pig heads and disappeared. He grabbed the meat. It was cool to the touch. As he stepped on the crates he felt the earth begin to tremble. The dark sky pulsated. The chug of the tractor rumbled in his ears. Diesel exhaust reached over and shoved him off the crates. He whirled in slow motion, buffeted by the cold wind.

He woke up on his back. The ground sucked the warmth right out of him. The first thing he saw was the oat grain on the dead pig's tongue. Then he looked up into a circle of faces.

"What are ya' doing lying down on the job, sitipoika? Tired already?" asked Rick's brother.

"I don't know. I got dizzy and fell down."

"Got dizzy, huh? Ha! I see some black stuff dribbling down your whiskers. I think you got too much nuuska poika. At least you had the sense enough to keep the meat from landing in the dirt. At first I thought you was doing a dance with that missus Ham Hock."

Surprised, David looked at the meat. He held it safely cradled to his chest. Someone took the meat from him. He rolled to his knees, spit out the rest of his snuff, then stood. His ears rang.

"Nuuska poika is up," crowed Rick. "One pig left to slaughter."

Rodney entered the pen. The last pig looked at him. Rodney shook the oats. The pig stepped forward, but shook its head and retreated to a far corner of the pen. Rodney clucked his tongue. "Come on, sika," he murmured in a low voice.

The pig wanted oats. A lifetime of eating propelled it to the bucket. But the pig also wanted to live. Rodney kept talking reassuringly. Haltingly the pig approached the bucket, stopping to snuff the air. After a few false starts the pig lowered its head to eat. Rodney lifted the gun. The pig jerked its head out of the oats and ran squealing over the frozen mud.

Rodney did not follow. Instead he kept talking in a low voice. "Come on now, don't be stubborn. Here, here, have some oats."

The pig inched forward. Rodney aimed. He pulled the trigger. The pig grunted and jerked. The gun's report bucked off the low sky. The pig stumbled to its knees swinging its head ponderously to and fro. Blood trickled into its eyes. Suddenly the pig lurched to its feet and trotted around the pen worrying its head trying to shake the red, red blood out of its eyes.

The pig and Rodney danced a life and death waltz. The tractor chugged the one-two-three tempo. Rodney moved closer. The pig moved away. The pig waltzed toward Rodney. Rodney aimed. The pig danced away. At last the pig came too close. **BLAM!**

Something was wrong! The pig still danced, only now it was squealing a painful song. Rodney cursed. The pig squealed in high pitched pain, barely stopping to breath. Rodney cursed again. "The kids shouldn't be out here. Somebody get me a rifle. I need a bigger gun. You kids, go in the house!"

The children stood transfixed. None of them went in.

While Rick ran in to fetch a rifle, Rodney kept trying to aim with the pistol. Blood dripped. The cold wind blew. The tractor kept time. The big gun came. He pointed the rifle. On a downbeat the pig was dead, silenced forever. The meat saw severed the head.

David looked into the sky. Snowflakes, inches in diameter, whirled and floated in every portion of the three dimensional air. The snow fell harder. When David looked down he saw the third pig's head lined up next to the other two. Its eyes could not see the falling snow. The only sound was the wind. Even the tractor had been shut off.

David stared.

Three pigs' heads on a blanket of snow. The first's tongue held the oat grain and several snowflakes. The second's ears were frozen in flopped over positions. The third's blood covered eyes were closed. They did not see the urban butcher kick his empty coffee cup and walk away into the coming winter.

DOMINICANS AND FINNS

Bernice Koehler Johnson

The island of Hispaniola lies between the waters of the Atlantic Ocean and the Caribbean Sea, in what the Dominican national poet, Pedro Mir, calls "an unbelievable group of islands of sugar and alcohol." Floating between Cuba and Puerto Rico, it looks like a stubby-tailed sea monster with mouth agape. The mouth is part of Haiti on the eastern third of the island. The western two-thirds, the body and tail, make up the Dominican Republic. I'm in Santo Domingo, the capital.

Columbus called this the New World. Contrasted with my native Minnesota, it is a new and very different world indeed, with its giant flowers and many-hued green foliage, flattened-into-leather rats littering the streets, and poverty-stricken, friendly people.

On my way to the church where I teach English, I pass six-foot wide houses painted blue, red, green, yellow, and pink abutting the sidewalk, where naked children play in gutter water, downstream from dead rats. On side streets, insect-and-rodent-infested garbage lies heaped like living monuments to the poor, who stare at me from tilted-back chairs and smile tentatively, then broadly, as I return their gaze.

Peering into a *colmado*, one of the grocery-store bars that liven the street corners of Dominican cities, I see a brown-skinned boy slapping sticks together, keeping time to merengue music emanating from oversized loudspeakers. The inner me sways to the rhythm, but I restrain myself.

I'm teaching for the Evangelical Dominicana Church, which forbids dancing. So far, I have danced only with a four-year-old girl, at a concert in the park. That might have been the highlight of my stay. My memories might have revolved around dancing with a child and walking through streets adorned by flowers and lined with litter, my spirit swaying to forbidden rhythms; but then I visited the Samana Peninsula and met Irma, a Finn, like me.

We were on the dimly lit veranda of Samana's Hotel Docia. I was practicing embroidery for a class I taught in Santo Domingo. Irma sat in the rocker at my left, swigging on an oversized bottle of *Presidente* beer, and chatting with the night clerk. For a moment I thought she was a native Dominican, so fluent was her speech, but it was clear, Castilian Spanish, unlike the rolling island dialect.

The clerk said he had sixty-eight brothers and sisters. "*!Esto es barbaro!* That's barbarous!" she said. That's what I thought but did not say.

"Did your father have more than one wife?" she asked.

The clerk chuckled. "He had three women," he said.

"*!Esto es barbaro!*" She turned toward me for affirmation and I quietly agreed.

Irma introduced herself, said she was from Finland and had been in the Dominican Republic for nine months--teaching English in Santo Domingo, as I was. I told her how I don't take teaching assignments for more than two or three months; don't like to be gone longer than that from my eighty-five year old mother. Limiting my stay works like an insurance policy: if I don't like the assignment, or, if I get lonesome for family and friends, I can go home. I like the idea of staying longer though, of really getting to know a country and its culture. Irma was doing what I would like to do.

The next day Irma and I have lunch at a seaside restaurant. We both order fish soup, which is also popular in Finland. Night had concealed Irma's long-legged, high-cheek-boned beauty. She's younger than I, in her fifties maybe; and she resembles my mother's sister, Marie, a full-blooded Finn. She has the same near-brusque manner, the same reddish hair, the same kind eyes. But the iris of Irma's left eye looks as if it's divided down the middle, one side is gold, the other side is green. "I've got a strange eye, too" I say, pointing to the right one where two black stripes intersect the iris. "Maybe we're related."

I want to be related to Irma. I've just met her, but already I know that she's more like me than I am--more like friends say I am, when they call me "adventurous" or "gutsy." I'm pleased when she gives me her phone number in Santo Domingo. At sixty-four, I still surround myself with people I admire, hoping I'll become more like them.

Irma lives in a better neighborhood than I--the San Carlos barrio of Santo Domingo, near the Zona Colonial, which enchants her, as it does me, with its restored colonial buildings. Within its environs are the palace built in the 1500s by Columbus' son, Diego, when he was governor; the first hospital built in the Americas; and the first cathedral. That's where Irma and I meet the following Saturday--next to a statue of Columbus, his right index finger pointing to this island, where in the name of God, he commenced the eradication of the indigenous Taino and introduced Catholicism.

The religion held, and at least some of the natives revere the discoverer whose granite image stands outside the Santa Maria la Menor Cathedral where Irma and I will attend an official mass. It was supposed to start at 10:00, but the cathedral doors are locked. The few people standing outside appear to be foreigners like us, who believe that when a Dominican says ten o'clock, it means ten o'clock.

We find a table at an outdoor cafe across from the cathedral, and Irma asks about my Finnish heritage. I tell her Grandmother Emma's story: trained to care for dairy herds, she emigrated from Finland at the age of nineteen. But the only work she could find was cooking in a northern Minnesota lumber camp. A Finnish cattle trader wooed her away from the camp to care for his two children who stayed with him when his wife left. In time, he divorced his wife and married Emma. They had six children of their own. He died young, leaving her the children, a mortgaged farm, and mortgaged cattle.

Alternating sips of passion fruit juice with *cafe con leche*, I tell Irma how the bank officials came to take the cattle. How Emma swore at them: "How the hell do you expect me to take care of six kids, if you take the cows?" They repossessed the farm but left the cattle which she took with her to a humble rental farm. Emma became known in the countryside for the fine calves she raised.

At noon we see a rush of excitement spread through the growing crowd and hurry to a wall surrounding the cathedral. Like children, we scramble onto ornamental indentations a foothold wide and several feet above the ground--a big step for me, but I struggle up and peer through a niche at the top of wall just as President Leonel

Fernandez arrives.

I expect boos and hisses: Fernandez has been in office less than a year and has given himself a 3000% salary increase at a time when workmen are lobbying for minimum wage of $100.00 U.S. per month.

To my surprise, someone yells "*!Viva Fernandez!*"

"*!Viva la Republica Dominicana!*" Fernandez yells, waving in the direction of his admirer, and the crowd stirs in appreciation. Charisma. The politician's weapon and his armor.

Irma and I join the throng pushing into the cathedral behind him. We bypass the pews reserved for Supreme Court justices and senators and sit in the Appellate Court judges' pew, next to a couple of Spanish tourists as brash as we. Humidity seems to have pressed the oxygen out of the air. Light-headed with heat and the mind-numbing incantations of the priest, we bob up and down with the rest of the crowd.

At the conclusion of the mass, Fernandez walks down the aisle next to us. I attempt a photograph, but, when the pictures are developed, I've only captured three-quarters of his face: a sweaty, wrinkled forehead, slightly protruding right eye, and half-open mouth. He's lost his charismatic aura.

After the mass, we find an outdoor restaurant across from the *malecon*, the sidewalk that borders the sea, where the Atlantic salt water splashes against dancers undulating to frenzied, repetitive Caribbean rhythms blasting from huge, black speakers. It's March 2. Carnival time. Horned, red masked devils cavort beside the dancers. I want to join them. The volunteer coordinator for the Evangelical church had been worried about me. "No smoking, drinking, or dancing," she had said.

"No problem, except I do love to dance." I did not guarantee that my feet would stand still if an opportunity arose.

Irma likes to dance, too. When I tell her my story, her eyes open wide. "You haven't danced, not even the merengue?" she asks.

I shake my head "No."

"You must dance," she says.

We have Pepsi-Colas and vegetarian pizza, then push our way through the crowd to the east end of the *malecon*, claim a shady spot under a tree, and watch the parade: bands, military marching units and flower-covered floats. A man in tight blue jeans stands in the center of a float with loudspeakers blaring Caribbean music. He swivels his hips in rolling hula-hoop movements, thrusting his groin forward again and again in rhythmic motions. This must be why Evangelicals don't like dancing.

Irma tells me about a community of Finnish immigrants in Santo Domingo. Her friend, eighty-year old Hilka, emigrated from Finland with her parents when she was six years old. She's jobless, pension-less, and poor. Irma suggests the three of us travel together some weekend and she will pay Hilka's expenses.

Hilka defies the image of an eighty year old. Her hair is peroxided and permed into a frizz. She wears bright red lipstick and too tight polyester clothes. If I were guessing her occupation, I would say she was a whorehouse madam. But I like her immediately, she has an engaging manner and an easy laugh.

The three of us spend a weekend together, taking a bus, and then a Honda taxi to Jarabacoa. Two men are in front. The three of us pile into the back seat. I climb in first and rest my bag on my lap, then the bulky Hilka struggles in and crams her bag on top of mine. When Irma squeezes in, I'm squished into a sliver. But I like the idea of two and a half Finns: one from Finland, one from the Dominican Republic, and the half-Finn from Minnesota, mashed like rutabaga casserole into the back seat of a Japanese car.

We check into a hotel with a disco below--non-operating, the owner assures us--then spend the afternoon exploring Jarabacoa, starting with Salto de Biguate, a waterfall outside of town.

To get to the falls we must climb up and across huge gray boulders and follow a rope bridge over a river churning with white water. Hilka puffs behind us with a determined smile on her painted red lips. She catches up where a waterfall spills into a deep pool carved into gray rocks that slope sharply into the cold mountain water. No one is swimming.

Irma sheds her tee-shirt and slacks and, looking cold and vulnerable in a bright blue swimsuit, she inches down slippery rocks to the water's edge. Within a few footsteps, she is immersed up to her neck. Pushing her arms out and away from her body in the breast-stroke, she approaches the falls, living out my unachievable dream. I'm afraid of deep water. And I'm afraid for Irma swimming alone in this hole in the rocks. So is the lifeguard on the opposite side of the pool. He joins us, stands watching beside Hikla and me, and waits at the pool's edge until Irma returns. He leans into the rocks behind him and Irma takes his outstretched hand. Their bodies form graceful ballet arcs as he pulls her from the water.

That night, the hotel room floors throb with Caribbean Rock from the supposedly closed disco. I think about joining the dancers, consider the inappropriateness of an Evangelical church teacher cavorting to Caribbean rock, and fall asleep.

The next day we take a pick-up truck bus across a dusty, winding mountain road to Manabao, which looks like a set for a Western movie. Tethered burros stand next to a stable, ready to trek up Pico Duarte, the highest mountain in the Dominican Republic. There are four more establishments: a cock-fighting arena; a military barracks; a post office; and Dona Patria's restaurant, *colmado*, and boarding house--the only rental beds in town. Hilka remembers the place from a visit ten years earlier.

The tiny concrete-floored rooms are clean. Each holds only a bed and a chair. Candle stubs in sardine cans rest on the shuttered window ledges. Manabao has no electricity, telephones, or running water. It's like going back in time to the rustic Minnesota farm where I was born. And there are other ways in which I feel as if I've returned to the past.

Dona Patria is a Dominican, but she looks like Grandmother Emma. Her broad, fleshy body is housed in a loose, print dress, covered by an apron. Her wispy gray-black hair is pulled back from her face and knotted at her neck. It is a shock to realize that this grandmotherly woman is probably no older than I. Still, when we go into the kitchen and see round, flat loaves of casabe bread baking on an open hearth, I feel as though I'm in Grandmother Emma's summer house, waiting for the loaf of Finnish flat bread she will pull from the oven.

That afternoon we walk the dirt roads of Manabao. Children run out of small roadside houses and walk at our sides. In the evening, we visit the *colmado* where Irma and Hilka buy a bottle of *Don Armando* rum. I take a sip. The rum smells like brown sugar, tastes like it too, reminds me of the hot toddies my father fixed to cure winter colds. They have no fresh juice, so I drink canned pear juice, imported from the U.S. Townspeople drift in to see the foreigners. As dusk settles, Irma starts calling me Hilka, and I retreat to the dining room where a solar powered generator sheds a soft light on the oilcloth covered table.   Dona Patria brings me casabe bread and a glass of cold water.   A quirky but pleasant *deja vu* transforms the dimly lit dining room into Grandmother Emma's summer house where I ate flat bread by the light of a kerosene lamp.

The Sunday issue of the Santo Domingo *Listin Diario* is on the table.   I glance through the society section--a photographic record of long gowned, blond women and light skinned men dressed in black tuxedos, descendants of the conquerors.   The kind of people I've never seen in the Dominican Republic, where most have rich brown skin that reflects their mixed Indian, African, French and Spanish heritage.   It's befuddling--this glorification of light skin.   Stranger, almost, than being in Manabao with two Finlanders and a grandmother look-alike the same age as I.

I follow a flashlight path to my room, then light the sardine-tin candle and prop myself up in bed, balancing the tin and my book, *In the Time of the Butterflies*, on my lap.   I tent the mosquito net over my head and get lost in the story of the three beautiful and brave Mirabel sisters who worked to undermine former dictator, Trujillo, until he had them murdered by the military.   When the candle burns down, I light another.   Caribbean music from the *colmado* jounces against and through the wooden partitions of the abutting rooms.   I think about dressing and joining the party--maybe they're dancing. Instead, I stay with the Mirabels until my candle sputters against the bottom of the tin.

Irma and Hilka return as I'm drowsing off. They're laughing and talking Finnish. Irma fumbles against our adjoining wall as she tries to fasten her mosquito net and mutters a Spanish-Finnish curse: "*Saatana! El mosquitero no sirve! Saatana!*" *Saatana*, Grandmother Emma's curse. It had been shocking when she said it, though I never knew what it meant. In the middle of a Dominican night, it seems hilarious. The next day Irma says that terrible swear word, *Saatana*, simply means Satan.

The next night, in Jarabacoa, we visit Hilka's friend, Anna, who immigrated to the Dominican Republic from Finland when she was sixteen--sixty-seven years ago. She's a couple of years younger than my mother, but more fragile and feeble looking.

Anna was married to an American and lived in the States for seven years. She speaks excellent English, as well as Finnish and Spanish. With unwavering politeness, whenever she addresses me, she switches to English. She offers us drinks, serves brown-sugary *Don Armando* and Coca Cola. Her apartment is neat, well-ordered, and the bookcase is stacked with English-language books. Were it not for the *Don Armando* and the Latin American music floating through palm trees outside the open balcony door, I might be in Minnesota.

Soon Anna, Hilka, and Irma are talking Finnish. A particular kind of loneliness, latent since childhood, descends on me. It is the feeling I had when I stayed at Grandmother Emma's house, where Finnish was the only language spoken.

When I was a child, speaking one's ancestral language was a mark of inferiority. Such a person couldn't learn, couldn't adapt to the New World. So my brothers and I weren't taught Finnish. Since our father was German, we seldom heard Finnish. Except for an occasional word--meaningless out of context--the language swirling through the air is unintelligible to me.

Anna turns toward me for a moment and translates. Trujillo had his eye on her when she was a teenager. He wooed her younger sister, too. They rejected him though it was dangerous to do so. I add Anna to my roster of heroes, right up there with Grandmother Emma.

The next week Irma pulls a tendon in her ankle, but wraps it tightly and suggests another outing on the weekend. We travel to Santiago to visit Archimedes, a union member for whom Irma has great admiration. She describes him as hardworking and cheerful, despite being blacklisted by the government for his Socialistic politics. And, she says, he's a gracious host.

The last time she visited Archimedes and his family, Irma had been with a group of Finnish friends, one of whom was a beautiful, but obese blond woman. She pitied her, Irma said, because she had such a hard time walking. She could dance though, and was very popular with Archimedes' friends, who called her, *La Gorda*, "the fat one."

Archimedes meets us at our hotel in Santiago, and we take a taxi to the tiny home where he lives with his wife and three children, his wife's mother, his brother-in-law and another relative, a woman with two babies. They crowd around us, smiling and talking. Archimedes' wife serves fresh cantaloupe and he opens the *Don Armando* we brought him.   Soon rum-induced lightheartedness pervades my companions, and their carefree mood overtakes me. We wander to the house next door where a party is in progress.

The hostess, a baby in her arms, stands beside a handsome man sitting in a rocker, his left leg propped at right angles across his right knee, a near-empty glass in his hand. Archimedes fills it with *Don Armando*. The room is full of people. Two of them stand out: an exotic-looking, young Dominican woman, who is enchanted with my fair skin, and asks Irma to take our picture together; the other is an extremely tall, thin man with thick, curly black hair. In English, Irma says, "He's a wonderful dancer." Then she asks him to dance with me. He asks her to dance instead.

She shows him her bandaged ankle, and once again, entreats him to dance with me.   He looks embarrassed.   Then, on the supposition that I can't understand Spanish, he says, "*Ah, Irma. Mi, me gusta La Gorda.* 'I like the fat one.'"   Irma looks uncomfortable. She says nothing, until I laugh and tell her it's the first time I've been rejected for being too thin.

Then, to my delight, our host rises from his rocking chair and stands gallantly at my side.

"Would you like to dance, Madam?" he says in Spanish.

Boombox merengue fills the air.   I've never danced the merengue, but it's impossible not to follow him as, with bent knees and swivelling hips, he circles the small living room floor with me in his arms.

We dance until I beg to sit down.   Then he stands beside me and says, "When you wish to dance again, Madam, just advise me." Irma looks smug and happy, like my Aunt Marie looks when she gives me a special gift.

It's six months since I left the Dominican Republic, and I some-times wonder whether I will see or hear from Irma again. Maybe not. But she will live forever in my mind, her name in big letters on the roster of female heroes that help me find my way in the world-- generous, brave, and adventurous. The kind of person I would like to be.

THE CURE

Sheila J. Packa

When my mother lapsed into silence, I knew it was catastrophic. Her silence had always been like steam inside the pressure cooker she used to pickle beets. The jars in the pot, the pot on the gas ring, and the weight--the small, silver weight the shape of a milk can, on the vent--dancing. Dancing over pressure. Silence. I heard it whistling.

"You should see a doctor," I said. She had dark brown hair with fine silver threads, and skin folds on the outer corners of her eyes. Despite all her efforts to hide it, age has made her appear more Finnish. Her name, Siiri, means flower. But she doesn't look like a flower. She is turning into a Lapp, a small, square, dark-eyed crone. On another burner, she's boiling bones. Beet juice has spilled on top of the white porcelain stove and somehow eluded her notice.

She dismissed my suggestion with a fierce shake of her head. The table in front of us was spread with a white towel. On it, jars of pickled beets cooled. They were red violet, sterile, transparent, hard. On the counter near the sink, she's heaped the fibrous skins of beets. They are not be thrown away. Nothing is to be thrown away, only used. For compost, if nothing else.

I should try to apply that theory to the spoiled love affairs I've been in--turn them over with a shovel, add water, let the leftovers decompose, and one day, rich, black soil, suitable for planting. What I ought to do is garden and maybe one day a new love will spring up.

The rag rug beneath our feet is made from the cloth of dresses and shirts somebody somewhere must have danced in. I tapped my foot over a line of emerald green woven with a metallic silver, once a party dress.

Silence.

Since I left my last husband, I've got time on my hands. I've nothing to do except make things. I am a weaver of sorts. I weave what she tells me and what she doesn't, the past with now, her life with mine.

When Siiri was in the first grade of school, her tongue couldn't form the sounds of the English language. The school nurse said her tongue was too tight and sent the doctor to the house to cut the skin holding her tongue down in her mouth. When Siiri saw the long black car, with its round fenders and deep running boards, she ran upstairs and slid under the iron bed where she slept at night with two of her sisters. She heard his voice, proper English, in the front porch explaining the matter to her mother who could not understand more than the rudiments. Snip the skin below the tongue to loosen it and make English possible. Her mother asked questions of him in Finnish. He repeated himself. Then, she relented before the large black leather bag and let the doctor into the kitchen. The kitchen was directly below the bedroom.

Her mother asked her to come and see the doctor. Siiri pulled her feet and pressed her knees into the wire spring, and grasped the rail with her hands. She did not answer.

Then she heard her mother leading him to the stairs. She led him to the landing, his step following her step, all the way up to the second floor. Siiri could see their feet below the curtain dividing the two rooms. She could see her mother turning toward her bed and bringing him in. The curtain was pushed to the side. Such treachery!

"It has to be done," her mother told her, in Finnish.

"Ei. Ei. Ei. Ei!" she answered. The rapid 'no's' sounded like a high-pitched, wavering scream.

The doctor tried to grasp her ankles to pull her out but she curled up out of his reach. She fought. When he got ahold of her foot, she kicked him loose. He moved the bed, she moved with it, scrambling to stay out of reach. The mattress above the springs slid away, and he looked at her through the cage of the wire springs.

"No," she said, with clenched teeth.

"Don't you want to be a good student?" her mother asked her, in Finnish. "Do you want to be a second grader?"

"No."

The doctor sighed. He slid the mattress back into place. Maybe he ran out of time, or realized that if getting her out from under the bed was so difficult, it might be even more difficult to open her mouth. He turned the clasp on his black leather bag and went down the stairs. The door slammed. The car engine revved and then the sound faded. Siiri's brothers and sisters were downstairs, telling each other about the fight.

Her mother came back upstairs and told her she could come out now.

"I can't. My hair is caught in the bed spring," Siiri said woefully.

"Voi, voi," her mother said softly. She came back with a little pair of scissors and tried to reach the tangle, but she was too big to fit under the bed so she handed them to Siiri's sister. "Don't cut too much," she warned.

She cut Siiri free.

"Now look how funny you are," she said.

Siiri crept downstairs to the mirror. The short hair on the top of her head stood straight up with static electricity. She licked her palm and rubbed her hair, to make it lay down. Her mother took up the comb and ran it through her hair and brushed dust off her back.

"He was going to hurt me," she said to her mother but her mother looked away, disapproving.

"Just a little, to make you better," her mother answered. She put the comb down.

"Ho-ho," said her brother Valo. "He's going to get the sheriff and put you in jail."

Siiri hesitated, looking again at her mother. She was never sure if her brother was kidding or not.

"The doctor might come back," her mother said.

"I'm going to fix my tongue myself," she said. She stretched her tongue out at her brother.

"Farther," he said. "You're going to have to make it longer than that, and practice everyday, until you can speak English.

Their mother interrupted, and told Valo to empty the slop pail.

The next day, the school nurse caught her doing that in the

cloakroom.

"My brother told me I had to, "Siiri answered. With her free hand, she pulled up the stocking that was sagging. The school nurse never had stockings that sagged.

"Which brother?"

Siiri did not answer.

The nurse let go of her and picked up a large pointed green hat, down the front in black letters was the word, Dunce. She put the hat on Siiri's head.

"Tell your brother not to teach you anymore disobedience," she said. As soon as Siiri nodded, her cheeks bright red, the nurse turned away and left her. Siiri stood as still as a stone. The hat had a metal rim that pressed on her forehead, it was too high and she felt it ready to pitch itself from her head. One of her classmates brushed her shoulder as she went past. Her brother snickered.

"I forgot something," Siiri said suddenly. She turned and went out in the hall. The hat tipped and fell into her hands and she set it against the wall. The teacher was already in the classroom. Siiri walked swiftly out the front door and three miles down the dirt road back home. She came along the long narrow driveway, past the marshy ditches on both sides and into the kitchen.

Her mother was walking the baby. Wood was crackling inside the kitchen range, a large copper vat of water was heating.

"Because of this, the school nurse made me wear the dunce cap." Siiri stuck out her tongue.

"In school, you were doing that?" Her mother shook her head and swayed back and forth with the infant in her arms.

"Valo told me I should."

The baby squirmed then broke out in screams. Siiri's mother went to the pantry and took down a bottle of brandy, uncapped it, and then soaked a corner of a cloth with it. She gave it to the baby. Little by little, he stopped crying. Her mother gave him to Siiri, wiped her own face with the sleeve of her dress and let out a sigh.

"I have to start the wash," she said. She put the brandy on the shelf behind the other bottles. It was for medicinal use only, used secretly, and hidden from Siiri's father.

"Can I make cake?" Siiri asked her mother. She pointed to the bag of sugar and her mother shrugged. Siiri laid the baby on the floor so she could quickly sift the flour and sugar into the bowl. The recipe was in her head. She whipped the batter with a whisk until it was smooth and creamy. Then she poured it in a flat pan and slid it into the oven. Then she had an idea.

The pantry was a tiny room lined with shelves. Beneath the counter were the bins for flour and sugar. Next to those, in gunny sacks, were potatoes, carrots, and onions. The shelves were lined with canned peas and green beans and pickled beets. She pushed aside the bag of salt, the can of pepper, the vanilla and found the tonics: a can of bag balm, a cow's horn that her mother used for cupping in the sauna. The edge of the horn was sharp enough to break the skin and it was hollow, so the horn could be applied to a small laceration and excess blood removed. It was an old remedy that her mother rarely used. Next to the cow's horn was the shock box. Square, wooden, with two wires ending in copper electrodes, it was the cure for rheumatism. One had only to turn the crank to send an electric current to the hands holding the wires. It was good for all stiff joints. Her father swore to its effectiveness. Her brothers preferred it for torture. She found the castor oil right next to the cod liver oil and then reached up to the highest shelf for the empty bottles her mother always saved.

She filled the empty cod liver oil bottle with six spoonfuls of cod-liver oil. Then she took another empty cod liver bottle and put in castor oil. Every night, her mother dosed them with cod liver oil, from the littlest to the biggest and tonight would be the same. Only the bottle would go empty just before Valo, and then her mother would take the next one on the shelf and uh-oh, Valo might not be able to sleep through the night. As she capped the bottles, she heard her father come into the porch. Like always, he stomped his feet twice on the rug just outside the kitchen door and let out a string of curses for the barking dog who responded with short, sharp barks. Her father's weight fell against the bench. He was muttering. He pushed his back against the wall to bring himself back to his feet. Siiri picked up the startled baby, ran from the pantry and went upstairs.

A small iron grid, a heat grate, was nailed to the floor. When she opened it, she could see the kitchen below as if it were a little theater. Her father stumbled through the door and fell back, closing it with his body. He was darkened by the soot of a fire and dressed in wool pants with elastic suspenders over a red checked wool shirt. Ragged long underwear cuffs hung below his shirt sleeves. He took a chair and slid it behind his legs as he sat down.

Her mother came in behind him to get a load of laundry. She was ignoring him, that was easy to tell. She swung her basket around the table. He tried to catch her going past him, but she was too quick.

"What you got there under the apron?" he asked, peering at her rounded stomach.

"As if you don't know," she said. She put her basket down. Siiri nodded. All the kids knew it--another baby was coming.

He swung his arm out, reaching for her mother. She slapped him away. There were words. It was no different than the other times. Siiri closed the grate.

The baby was asleep again. She brought him to the bed and put him on top of the covers. By laying on the bed, she could see the top of the tree outside her window. The wind lifted the branches slightly, only a few leaves remained, wrinkled and dry. In the small patches of sky she could see, clouds gathered, becoming deeper and darker. She thought of the sky above the clouds, where the sun always shone, the stars always glimmered, and the moon always hung in its place. She would like to be up there, somehow. She would like to be a hawk, high and quiet in her own heaven with her own angels and the sister who had died at birth and all of the mothers before her own mother. The ones from Finland. She would like to see them all, to sail into their laps, to hear them sing, sing louder than the anger crashing like thunder below her. Strikes like lightening. Storms. And the smell of burnt cake.

The kids came home from school, from the barn, and hayshed. Siiri watched them from the upstairs window. Darkness filled the distance, making the spruce and tamarack in the swamp turn black. Her brothers and sisters gathered in the yard, pumped water on each other's hands, and splashed it on their faces. The metal plunger of the pump hiccoughed. The water spilled in the grass and the boards beneath the pump glistened. Their voices were in perpetual argument, 'make me' and 'don't think I can't.' The baby awakened and she carried him down.

"Look who's playing hookey," Valo said.

Her mother was stirring the pot. Siiri pushed between her sisters on the bench at the table. Her mother filled her bowl with boiled potatoes in a butter and cream sauce, then added a small poke of smoked fish. Siiri pulled the meat from the delicate ribcage of the bones and rubbed the oil between her fingers. Her brother's arm reached across the table, his fork ready to spear one of her potatoes. She brought her arms down around her dish.

"Valo..." warned her mother.

"I made you some cake," Siiri said.

Her mother had cut away the burnt corners of the cake and lifted the slices onto a big plate. Valo took a piece that crumbled before he got it to his mouth. He ate it slowly, chewing slower and slower. He grinned at her, showing how he had turned it to paste in his mouth.

After the sisters washed dishes, it was time for fish oil. Siiri's mother found the bottle of cod liver oil and dosed six children, all in a row. The bottle went empty exactly as Siiri planned, before Valo.

"Get me another cod liver oil." her mother said to her.

"I don't want any," Valo said.

"It's good for you. You won't get sick if you have some," her mother said, gesturing again to Siiri. Siiri went to the pantry and took the castor oil she'd disguised in the cod liver oil bottle and brought it to her mother.

"I won't get sick anyway," Valo said.

"Give it to me, then," her father ordered. Siiri watched helplessly as her mother poured out a spoon for him and he swallowed it.

She went to get her arithmetic. She sharpened her pencil with a paring knife and licked the point before putting her name at the top of the paper. They were learning addition, how to carry a number. She worked laboriously on her work, not because she did not know how to solve the problems, but because she was aware of her father watching as she counted the sums on her fingers. Carry the one, she told herself. Carry the two. Carry the three. She frowned when she came to the story problems. Story problems were more difficult than any others. She began swinging her foot, to the right and left. Her father got up from his chair and looked over her paper.

"What's it say?" he asked.

"Samuel had one-hundred and fourteen oranges. He sold a

third of them to his friend for three cents apiece.."

"So this Samuel--what does he do with the profit?" her father asked.

"I don't know," she whispered.

"Oh you don't know, do you? And neither do you ask. Is that what they teach in school, not to ask?"

"It's arithmetic," she said.

Her father laughed. He shifted on his feet, rubbed his hand along his shirt.

"That's not just arithmetic," he said. The hoarseness in his voice cleared and he paced in the room. Her brother who was on the floor working on his schoolwork pulled back his feet so they wouldn't be trod upon. Valo's glance caught Siiri's, as if to say, here we go again. Their father continued. "Nothing is just arithmetic. It's also history and science and something else besides. Nobody will tell you everything. You have to think. Two and two don't always make four. Remember that, little girl."

He abruptly turned and went through the kitchen, out the door, down the steps and the path toward the outhouse. Inside her trembling body, she felt a tiny bubble of glee that could neither rise nor break. She felt it there, nudging her heart, even after her mother called her to help fold the diapers.

"Life is hard," her mother told her. "It's work. There's no end to the work."

Siiri could hear the slam of the outhouse door.

"But I help, don't I mother?" she said.

"Why don't you call me Äiti? I called my mother Äiti, she called hers Äiti, all way back. If you knew your grandmother, she'd have you call her Iso-äiti."

"But this is America," Siiri said, taking a diaper and folding it, exactly in the way that her mother had shown her.

"This is Toivola," her mother said.

"Why did our family come here, anyway?"

"Your father left Finland because his stepmother, in a fit of meanness, broke his accordion. He came to Michigan with a brand new one, with buttons. I fell in love with his music and married him. But I was only a girl of sixteen, who couldn't tell the difference between a man and his music.

If he hadn't been a Red Finn, he might have settled down to work in the mine. He would have gone to church on Sundays and stayed away from the bottle. He wouldn't have been unionizing, nor would he have been blacklisted for instigating strikes." Her mother paused, looking far off into the past. "If you are barred from the company, you can't live in a company house, or trade at the company store. They turned us out."

"Who did?" Siiri asked.

"The goons," her mother answered. "We came here to Toivola, with his new accordion. This forty acres of rocks and swamp--this poor farm. He could never play a song beautiful enough to make up for all this. Trees had to be cut. Stumps had to be pulled out with a team of horses or blown up with dynamite. Ditches had to be dug to drain the lowland fields. I lost a baby in that field. After, I made Pentti go and talk to the foreman of the iron mine but he wouldn't hire him. It seems the blacklist can follow us anywhere that we go. We've had bad luck."

"I'm losing my guts," said Pentti. He stood in the open door with his suspenders loose. Äiti ignored him and kept on.

"Not enough food on the table."

"Pretty soon I'm going to drop dead. All that will be left of me is a pile of crap."

Siiri swallowed nervously. She wondered if mineral oil could kill somebody.

"No woman to help birth the babies," her mother added.

"That will be your bad luck then," Pentti said.

"But the most important thing in the world to Pentti Keinonen is whiskey."

He rocked on his heels and abruptly left the house and went back down to the outhouse. He did not come back inside.

When the moon came out, Pentti emerged from the shadows. He took up his accordion and stood on the stump in the yard. Mosquitoes swarmed him, biting through the red wool of his shirt, but he didn't feel the bites. If he played loud enough, he couldn't hear the insects whining. The silver filigree of his instrument gleamed more sharply than the ivory keys. Didn't he force the forest to recede, didn't he raise the house and barn? Didn't he witch the water and dig the well? Didn't he once make his wife want to dance? She went outside in her nightgown to drag him to bed.

"Wait," he said, scuffling with her. He was tipsy and swayed precariously when she took his arm. Dancing was out of the question. It was as if he had balance only by himself now.

"I'll carry it," she said, taking the straps and lifting the weight of the accordion.

"Watch out, Mother," he said, as he fell backwards on the roots of the stump that he hadn't pulled out.

"I have to watch out," her mother said, as she brought the accordion into the house and put it away. "Drunks never get hurt."

He was singing now, hoarsely, losing the rhythms. After awhile, he was silent.

The next morning, Pentti was found in the kitchen between the woodbox and the stove. He startled out of his slumber when Siiri's mother lifted the stove grate and dropped in a chunk of wood.

"Time to eat," she told him.

He pulled himself up to the table, shaking visibly. She set a loaf of bread in front of him. She put a pot of coffee on the stovetop; she adjusted the dampers. Then she went into the pantry. He reeked of the outhouse and moonshine. He was mumbling and peering at the chunks of bread he'd torn off.

She put the butter on the table and tried to take the bread out of his hands.

He jerked and dropped the bread. It slid beneath his boots, crumbs caught in the broken laces. His fingers plucked at his pantlegs.

"I did a bad thing." Siiri went up to her father. "It wasn't cod liver oil that you took, but mineral oil. Maybe there's something else you can take, so you don't die."

He grimaced, squinted, and then tore furiously at his legs, stamping the bread beneath his heels. He looked at her but didn't see her. His body twitched dramatically, as if he were a puppet on invisible string.

Äiti ran her palms down her apron, watching him. She put her hand on his shoulder; he leapt back with alarm.

"All right," she said, softly, backing away. She came back with the bottle of brandy, for medicinal purposes only. She poured him a drink. Siiri and her brothers and sisters had filed down the stairs but stayed back. They watched him turn the glass in his hand as if he were examining an unfamiliar object.

"Drink it," she said.

He swallowed the brandy all at once and sputtered.

The children waited. He hadn't seem them.

Suddenly, he got up, knocking over the chair over as he rose, but he didn't put it right. He kept on going, out of the porch, out into the field, in a blind run.

"Should I go after him?" Valo asked, going toward the door.

"After I get something in your stomach," his mother said, taking out the oatmeal pot and filling it with water. The dipper clanged in the water pail. She hadn't known what else to do, except give Pentti that shot of brandy. She went around the kitchen twice, uselessly, as the children watched her. She went into the pantry twice and came back each time empty-handed.

It's the old story. Same old, same old.

In her kitchen, many years later, I could smell vinegar in her hair. Beets. I think of cucumbers. Herring. Pigsfeet. She loved pickled things. She put up untold numbers of things. Her cupboards were full, then empty, then full, perpetual. Hardly anything went bad because she was good at it. But if it did, she could tell. The lid of the Mason jar would click. The contents might be cloudy. She has a finely developed sense of smell. She swears she can smell botulism or salmonella, or anything for that matter. Bacteria. All she needs is one whiff to know whether her father had some liquor. Her father, my father, me. I haven't. I quit drinking.

"Alice, all I need is a sauna," she says. Steam, that's her answer to most things.

She built a fire in the sauna. Outside the sauna walls, in the yard, one could hear the water in the boiler, bubbling. The sauna, pronounced sow (rhymes with cow) - na. The sauna is a Finnish bathing ritual. How many other cultures have such a thing? The Japanese, the Turks. The sauna is the place of many transformations. In it, babies were born, the dead are prepared for burial. The fire. The water. Steam. Everything can be washed down. In the fall, deer are butchered. Fire, water, steam. Everything can be washed down, and everybody. It was the first building a Finn built on his piece of property, in the old days. Anyone who has taken a sauna knows she comes out looking younger, her skin more taut and pink. It gives the sense of well-being, and the certainty of being clean. Maybe she's right. The sauna might cure her and it might cure me.

I looked at the stack of records on the stereo and set the button to 78 rpm. *Pistol Packin' Mama* was the name of one of the records I used to always listen to. The refrain went: *Lay that pistol, down, ma, lay that pistol down, pistol packing mama, lay that pistol down.* Now there was a woman who could dish out as much trouble as she got.

Back in 1930, Siiri's mother gave up waiting for Pentti to come out of the woodshed and milk the cows. The cows knew who she was anyway; they wouldn't kick her. She wouldn't lose the baby inside just by bending over to do the milking. She tied a clean diaper around her head as a scarf. If it was up to him, the cows would dry up. The empty pail swung from her hand. Her apron barely reached around the girth of her body. The baby inside kicked. She tied the cow's tail up with a length a rope hung from the low beam overhead, and then she threw hay down for the cow to eat. She took a tiny three legged stool and sat down with effort, pulling the teats on the udder. You can't fool a cow. They knew if you were upset or mad and could keep their milk from letting down. She needed to calm herself, steady her hands. She stroked the smooth skin until the milk began to spray in the bucket. The barn cats came to beg when they heard the sound, so she squirted a fine stream into their faces. She milked all three cows, but instead of lowering the pail of milk into the well to cool, she brought it up the slope to the woodshed, flung open the door, and threw the contents onto Pentti who was on the floor, snoring loudly.

"Good morning," she said.

He jumped up and grabbed her arm but fell back as soon as he rose. She avoided falling with him, but then she stumbled over a brown bottle on the floor and fell forward, her shoulders over the threshold of the door.

Liquor poured from the spilled bottle before he snatched the bottle up and put it away, next to a chunk of wood. The buckle of his rubber boot had torn her stocking. He rubbed his eyes. The white milk was washing along the plank floor, full of grit and bits of bark. A vise-like cramp gripped her body.

"Saatana perkele," he said. He kicked the milk pail out of the open door. They were both wet. The smell of the warm milk made him sick. And then, as if his mind was just beginning to clear, he asked her if she was all right.

Waves of pain shot through her stomach and back. She got herself to her knees and then to her feet. She held the doorway, steadying herself. She felt something inside of her, like a tear ripping from the top of the thigh all the way up to her navel. She touched her stomach, but she was all in one piece on the outside. Then fluid broke and soaked the tops of her stockings and her shoes.

"Ei," she said. But he had already fallen back into his stupor.

She let go of the doorway and ran, bent nearly in half, to the sauna. Three of her children were pulling on the dog in the path in front of her.

"Stay right here. Äiti has to go to the sauna and get another baby."

"Me too," said the toddler.

"No. Play with the puppy." Once inside the sauna, she grabbed the bench and sat while another contraction gripped her.

The children had followed and stood in a semicircle around her.

"Äiti?" the boy said.

"Äiti's okay," she answered, letting her breath out once again. She brought herself to the bench in the steam room and reassured them once again. She asked them to get the oldest girl, Ina, and they ran to the house.

She grabbed a towel from the peg on the door and waited for the next pain to subside. She panted, tried to get up and then sank down again. She pulled off her wet and blood-tinged stocking and underwear and threw them on the floor. She tried to get the towel down. The boards smelled of cedar and faintly, of naphtha soap. Perspiration dripped from her face though the room was chilly. She could see the baby's head crowning.

Arghh. She pushed with all her strength. The head emerged. She pushed again and it slid out, slippery as a fish, gasping at the air. He began crying.

"Shhh," she said, reaching for him. A contraction clamped her once again and the afterbirth slid out. She had nothing within her reach to clamp the cord. Her hand ran along the surface of the higher bench, where she had leaned her shoulder. One stray clothespin. She tried to push it on the umbilical cord, but the pin was too small. She laid the baby on the towel on the floor next to the bench and tried to reach toward the water tank, to get a little to clean herself off, but a weakness came over her and little by little, the sunlight in the window dimmed and then went completely out.

"Where's Äiti?" Ina asked the younger children when she came home. She had stayed after school to try out for a play. Her school satchel was in her hand. They loved her satchel and often looked for any leftovers from her lunch. Sometimes she saved things for them, a piece of bread or a thin slice of squeaky cheese.

"I ate my lunch. See--all gone."

The news made them all start crying. The house was silent, the kitchen stove cold.

"I'm hungry," one of the younger ones said.

"Hungry," echoed another. He had taken off his diaper by himself.

Ina remembered that the older children were going to the neighbors that night, to help tear more rags for the rug loom. She asked the young ones where Äiti was.

"Sauna." The youngest one, said, clearly.

Ina took a hurricane lamp out to the dark sauna and found the ninth baby. He was the color of the cement floor. Her mother was on the bench, one arm flung out toward him. Her eyelids fluttered at the sudden brightness of the lamp.

"The baby," she said, almost as if she was asking.

Ina picked up the infant and put it in her mother's arms. He moved. He was alive, barely.

"Cut the cord dear," her mother said. She unbuttoned her dress and held the baby close to her breast. She touched his cheek and he turned toward her, searching for the nipple. He made a little sound between a grunt and a cough, lost the nipple and found it again. Ina could hear him breathing through his nose; he was noisy, struggling.

"With what?" Ina asked, searching the dressing room. She

picked up the small hatchet used to make kindling and a chunk of firewood. She set the wood on the bench beside her mother, set the cord--a mess of blood and tissue lay at the end of it--against the wood.

"Go ahead. It'll be all right," her mother said.

She sawed the cord with the sharp edge of the hatchet. It was tough and not easily severed so she brought the hatchet down hard and separated him from the afterbirth. Her mother rubbed the baby's arms and legs with her hand.

The older children had followed Ina to the sauna. They wanted to see.

"Can I name him?" Siiri asked, pushing ahead of them.

"Take them in the house for awhile." Ina shut the door of the steam room. Her knees shook. She was sixteen. It was not the first time that she had been there when a brother or sister had come into the world, but this time she was the only one who was there. Where was her father? She made a fire in the stove to warm her mother and brother, then reached to the water tank to pull up dippers of water to wash down the drying red stains on the floor. There was a body smell, like an animal's, that reminded her of the cattle. She pushed the afterbirth into an old newspaper. It squished as she wrapped it. The fire was roaring inside the belly of the stove, the metal of the sides and stovepipe began to heat. She left the dampers open and took up the bar of soap.

"Can I name him Christopher?" He was born on Christopher Columbus Day." Siiri knelt close to the week-old baby and smelled his just-birthed, powdery smell. To her, the baby's birth was timely, on a holiday no less American than Independence Day. She took it as a sign of good luck.

"What an odd name. But he is already named Tervo," her mother said. She was up and around as usual, making soup as she talked.

Pentti was in the bedroom. He was finally going around the bend. His head was full of crazy notions and he wouldn't eat. The neighbor men had been over to help milk the cows and clean the barn. The children were afraid of their father. He talked a lot of murderous nonsense when the delirium tremens came over him. Their mother poured his shots of liquor just to keep him quiet. He seemed not to understand that the baby had been born.

"Tervo isn't the name for an American citizen," Siiri said. She felt ashamed of her family: her mother who wouldn't speak English, the mutterings of her father, and her brothers and sisters who went to the Young Communist Camp at the Mesaba Cooperative Park near Hibbing.

Her mother reassured her that Finnish people could indeed be citizens, ever since Judge William A. Cant of the United States District Court sitting in Duluth, Minnesota, January 17, 1908, declared that though perhaps Finns had been 'Mongols' in the past, they were now among the whitest people in Europe and deserved citizenship.

"Then why did our uncle go to the Soviet Union to be a communist?" Siiri asked.

"He went because they needed farmers," her mother said firmly. The family was worried about him; they had not heard anything for so long.

"Have some rieska." Her mother cut thin slices from the dense dark rye bread on the counter and ladled a bowl of soup for Pentti. She called him to eat. It was one of his tranquil days. The baby, who was in the other room in a battered bassinet near the oil stove, began to yell.

Pentti turned his head at the sound.

"Do you want to see him now?" Siiri asked.

"Don't bother your father," her mother said.

"He's puny," Siiri went on.

Her father stopped chewing. He looked toward the window. His eyes had a bright light in them.

"When you're better," her mother told him. "Then, you can play with the new baby."

"Let's see him," Pentti said.

Siiri went to the bassinet. Her brother was as light as a shuck of corn in her arms. She showed him to her father.

Her mother tried to feed Pentti more soup, but he pushed the spoon away with his hand. His face was working, as if he were struggling with several emotions.

"It's Tervo," her mother whispered.

Pentti clicked his tongue. He was dark and gnarled, and smelled of woodsmoke and spirits. He had bad teeth.

The baby opened his eyes and stared toward the kerosene lamp.

"What's one more? There's always room for a baby." Her mother nudged Pentti because he was staring. She still had the spoonful of broth poised in the air when he slammed his fist down against the table. Siiri jerked away, shielding her new brother.

All of sudden, madness came over Pentti. His wife put his hand out to steady him and he leaned forward, as if he was leaning into the cold winter wind that just began to blow outside. He went to the window and then leaned against it. The glass bowed and shattered with a loud crack, falling with him, outside to the ground.

Siiri described it, over and over, to her brothers and sisters that night upstairs, in the darkness of their rooms.

"He could have killed himself," she said.

"Was there anything outside that he was going after?" one asked her.

"Maybe he remembered something from the day that Tervo was born," another said.

"He was drunk," Valo said. He had spent the afternoon nailing boards across the window frame to stop the cold air from coming in.

"He cut his whole body," Siiri said again. "Mother had to tear up rags to cover him."

"Did she sew him up with her darning needle?" a sister asked, muffling an odd laugh.

"No, she glued him together with balsam pitch," Siiri answered.

"And gave him a drink. No, she gave him two drinks because now he leaks like a sieve!" Valo kicked the wall.

"Nukkumaan." Ina wanted to put a stop to the talking. They were all quiet at once. The clock was ticking and the wind outside was picking up, pushing at the wall they slept near. Downstairs, their parents were asleep, Pentti on the side next to the wall and their mother on the edge. The baby's bassinet was downstairs too, still in the room where there was an oil stove, the warmest room. In the kitchen, the dog was dreaming. The room was cold, getting colder, but under the blanket with her sisters, it was warm.

"But I'm not tired," said one of the smaller ones to nobody in particular, a long time after the moment when their bodies had relaxed and settled down near the edge of sleep.

There was a knock on the door once, twice. Siiri could hear her mother rising and going into the kitchen.

"Who is it?" she asked. And when she heard the voice of Pentti's brother, the uncle who had gone to the Soviet Union, she flung open the door.

Siiri slid out of bed and down the stairs. Her mother heard her and sent her back, telling her she could see him in the morning. But once back in bed, she listened as best she could.

"Things were terrible there," he said, his low voice still audible in the quiet house. And he could not have gotten out if he had not hidden his American money inside a hollow he'd made in his shovel handle.

Her mother whispered, "It was a good thing you could look ahead. A good thing that you got clear of that."

One of the deeper silences of the house was the accordion. Before, Pentti's hands climbed up and down the ivory buttons as his arms opened and closed the bellows. The accordion breathed its polkas and folk songs easily, as if it were the throat of the old country. The silver filigree and wooden fretwork beside the rows of buttons fascinated Siiri, as did the silver corners of the bellows. When the bellows opened, a white diamond appeared. On the side opposite the ivory buttons were rows of small dark blood red buttons that her father played with his left hand. She found an ornate script carved in ebony, barely visible but she could feel it with her fingertips. Made in France.

He played to distract a fussy child or sometimes played a waltz for Äiti, for old times' sake, and sometimes he played the accordion with his brother singing, but not now. Since his brother came back, he was in a darker mood. The instrument remained snapped in the tiny straps and inside the leather case, lined with crushed red velvet, the latches fastened.

Now that Pentti was bedridden, recovering from the numerous gashes of the window, and oppressed by the heavy silence, Siiri took it upon herself to bring out the accordion and give it to him. He laid his hands listlessly across it.

"Do you think you could play it?" she asked.

He cocked his head away from her, as if listening to some music she couldn't hear. For a long time, she had trained her tongue in the new ways of the public grammar school, speaking no Finnish, even dreaming in the new language. Her Finnishness was inside her, enclosed like a bird in a dovecote. With her tongue to release it, it beat its wings against the walls of her ribs, and in her fingertips. It felt like fear.

"Do you think you could teach me?" she asked in Finnish, running her hand over the ivories.

He had a slash across his face that went over his forehead, through his brushy eyebrow and down his cheek, stopping at his throat. It was inflamed and his eye was swollen shut. He glared at her with his one good eye.

She did not flinch.

"Listen," he said. And she listened to what she knew was silence.

"Listen inside of here." He tapped her chest bone with his fingers. She sat on the bed and slipped her arms into the worn leather straps. She unsnapped the snaps and the instrument sprung loose, inhaling. He put her hands on the keys and she closed her eyes.

"Play," he said.

She pressed a few notes. It was awkward. The silver metal corners of the bellows gouged in her thighs. Her hands wandered, lost, finding jarring notes. Then she found a note she recognized, and another, haltingly; finding it was a path to the polka that she heard him play countless times.

"Both hands." He pressed the fingers of her left hand on the red buttons.

The accordion began to conjure an earlier time, when her father was still hewing timbers. She opened her eyes. His eye was moist.

It was an iron-cold winter. The uncle stayed to help out with the farm. The fluttering inside Siiri's hands got worse. The snow closed the roads for days before the plows broke through. When the frost bit the children's fingers, their mother kept them in. They huddled around the woodstove that burned hard, but only managed to heat two rooms.

There was a hot and dry, crackling and biting thirst in Pentti's throat and he couldn't quench it. By the spring, he was haggard with weight loss and seemed to keep a two or three days growth of beard on his creased face. Red veins shot through his eyes. He was running short of liquor. The children fled from him because he often had the snakes.

The oldest four children went to check the rabbit snares. It was the first Saturday of April. They heard the explosion and retort of a gun. Valo turned and ran back toward the house, ahead of Siiri and her sisters, following the same tracks in the snow.

Pentti stood on a stump in the backyard, aiming his rifle past the barn into the place where the lowland woods turned to swamp. He was aiming his rifle at them.

"What's he shooting," Ina said.

"Bears," Valo said. "Karhu."

"He doesn't realize it's us," she said.

"Get away!" He's gone berserk!" Äiti shouted at them from the door of the house. She pointed toward the woods.

The other children slipped around the woodshed, behind the outhouse and to the back of the barn, sliding against the iron discs of the farm implement.

"Saatana perkele!" Pentti turned toward the barn. He cocked the gun and put another shell into it.

Äiti threw herself against him, knocking him off the stump. He went down hard and she took the gun and rose. He grabbed her, pulled her down. Siiri couldn't see what happened next. A shot rang out. The trees echoed. Äiti rose again, staggered, went down on her knees. Pentti lay like a stone. He was dark; he looked like he had slept in a bed of ashes.

"Äiti?" called Valo.

Their uncle ran past the children to their mother, he turned and bent down over his brother, as if to shield him or shield them.

The second youngest child came out of the house, wearing a t-shirt and diaper, carrying an empty bottle of milk. He was barefooted and stopped before he put his feet to the cold ground. The sky was clouded. Flakes of snow drifted aimlessly.

Valo stopped five feet away.

"Should I get the doctor," he asked, panting, looking away.

His mother rose from the dark place on the ground.

"Ei," she said. She pushed away the dog and took hold Valo's shoulder.

"Was it an accident?" Siiri felt fluttering all over her body now, not just in her hands, but in her legs and head, in her throat and inside her ears. Something inside her told her this was her fault, that since the mineral oil, he had become worse and worse.

Äiti looked at her children, counted them by putting her hand out to each one's shoulder. She put her hand on Siiri. She was dazed. Her face was white as snow.

Many years later, when my mother and my aunts talk about it, they talk in Finnish, the language I don't understand. I'm not all clear about what happened. Maybe he died that day because that was the day her stories stopped, or maybe he died later, of something else and the remaining memories are preserved, kept away from me on a high shelf. Maybe she thinks of him as sealed in a bottle, red violet, briny, gone bad.

My mother turned off the burner under the pot of bones. She plucked one and it clanked on the plate, steaming. She took up a knife and inserted it into the middle, taking out the marrow and spreading it over a cracker. She offered some to me. But I turned my head, made a face, and said, "Maybe later."

SMOKY HILLS STORIES

Jake Harvala

Footprints

Winter, 1961

Cold winter. Drifting snow type winter in Smoky Hills of northern Minnesota. A new snow, heavy, lies between the house and the winter home of the hand-milked cows. The barn is probably seventy yards from the house. A path, single file, usually is visible. Of course after a heavy snow, the crooked human path takes a few days to develop.

Telephone attached to the wall. Party line. Hytone. Finnish farmers progressing. The phone rings. An order is given by a sister to deliver a message to new sister-in-law, Priscilla. In a short sleeved from a long sleeved hand-me-down sweatshirt, eight year old Jacob runs to the barn where Priscilla is entertaining the Saturday morning milkers.

Priscilla offers a question before young Jacob can deliver his message. "Where are your shoes? You are barefoot and will freeze your feet."

Jacob is standing on a warm piece of hay. He replies, "Oh, that's ok, I'll just run back to the house in the same footprints that I made when I ran here."

Rag Rugs

Summer 1964, Penn Avenue, Minneapolis, Minnesota

Young Jacob, now eleven years old, youngest of eight children, gets to visit the city with the brother and sister-in-law, Priscilla. They lived in a second floor apartment, duplex type, one on top of the other. There was a red deck off the back, a grassy back yard, and a couple of shade trees.

As part of the deal of being in the city, Jacob was delegated some chores. Monday Morning, 10 AM formation. Priscilla suggests that he take the carpets (the handmade rugs all the Finns in the American North seem to have) and shake them out and toss 'em over the rail. Easy enough, as he had done this at home, only at ground level.

Well, there were about ten rugs, I suppose, and even though he thought the instructions were odd, he got the job done. Priscilla asked him if he was done as she is walked to the deck for inspection. To her dismay, the rugs were nowhere to be seen on the rail, but scattered haphazardly on the green summer ground. She asked in disgust, "Why are all the rugs on the ground?"

Young Jacob replied, "You told me to shake the rugs and throw 'em over the rail. I thought that was a bit odd, but maybe that's how you do it in the city."

Priscilla laughed. The only extra effort, though, was they had to go down the front entry and haul up the rugs.

Cool!

Summer, 1967 Los Angeles, California

Now I'm thirteen with the crookedest front upper six teeth you've ever seen. Shit. I tried never to smile.

I was told, many years later, that I was shipped off to California with my sister and her family for three weeks, "to find myself." What? I was thirteen. The buzz phrase of the 60's, I guess. I did find myself in California, for sure. I looked down at my two feet planted firmly on the ground, with the Hollywood Hills sign in my horizon, and Yep, this is California. LA, 1967. I didn't realize what that trip meant until years later. Sunset Strip, the ocean, straight teeth, music, anti-war sympathizers, peace, love, and war, LA was a pretty groovy trip.

Just the radio station alone (KHJ) was far, far better than what we could ever pick up from Fargo-KQWB or KFYR in Bismarck or somewhere in Western N.D. In the winter we did get WLS out of Chicago and a station out of Oklahoma City, but those days are another story.

There were LA moments. My sis, Judy and her then husband drove me up to Big Bear. I jumped into icy mountain water. They had a daughter who was probably eighteen months old. I stayed in her room. She would stand up in the crib in the morning and wake me up by saying quite sternly, "Hey boy, hey boy, wake up. Hey boy, hey boy, wake up."

Below my sister's apartment (technically Culver City) lived a gentleman who was an actor. Not a famous one, but one who made a living at it, I guess. He drove a two-seater, no roof automobile that looked real fancy. Like an older car. Spoke wheels and big round fenders over the wheels. When he retired it for the night, he snapped a vinyl cover over the top from door to door. Let's call him John, because I think that's what his name was. John knew I was from a dairy, rock farm with eight cows in Smoky Hills, Minnesota.

After being in LA for a couple weeks, John takes me for the day. Cool! I liked John. He didn't make me talk. I could speak when I wanted, ask any question, I was just along for the ride. My ride, although I think he enjoyed the sights as well. John would point things out to me that I didn't have the sense to ask. Plus I trusted him in his two-seater car. He wasn't weird with me, he wasn't drinking, and he kept his hands to himself. John drove to the beach. I had been there before with my sister and brother-in-law, but this was different. We looked at gals in our own quiet ways. We listened to the ocean. We felt the air.

We went to Jack-in-the-Box for lunch. Then we got into the meat and potatoes of the tour. Sunset Boulevard. Hundreds maybe thousands of hippies. I recall a sit-in, love-in in a park in and around Pandora's Box. People smokin pot, handing out flowers, saying peace not war. We drove through the area at a very moderate speed. Somehow John knew I would remember that day in July of 1967.

After I returned home to the Smoky Hills, in that winter of 1967, I saw John as an extra with a small speaking part with Bill Dana playing Jose Jiminez. Cool.

California wasn't the trip to end all trips, but it certainly ranks up there as I reached my twenties and realized not everyone got to be in LA in 1967.

Crooked Teeth

Smoky Hills, 1968

I am a teenager and still have the crookedest six front upper teeth you've ever seen. At the school's yearly nurse check-up, orthodontia was recommended to my parents on a note sent home. Oh really!

My mother tried. My mother succeeded. Let's face it, braces to the family income wasn't convenient.

My mother took me to the family dentist, Dr. Schuckart, (bless his soul), and pleaded with him to put braces on her child. Schuckart said, "I'm not an orthodontist."

My mother said, "You sure are and a pretty darn good dentist." He said he would do some reading and get back to us.

A couple of weeks later, Dr. Schuckart called and agreed to experiment with me and put braces on my top row for $100.00. I sat in Dr. Schuckhart's dentist chair while he hammered the caps on my teeth till my gums bled. Cinching the wires tighter and bending the wires back after a tightening would leave a sharp wire end that would cut into the back of my cheek. "It hurt a little," I'd tell him. I didn't want to disappoint him. I told him I was eager to have it done.

The hundred dollars included the retainer, which I later stepped on and broke while shooting baskets in the hay loft. See when you have a retainer and you run, saliva builds up. Well, it just didn't feel right. So I put it in my shirt pocket, and the retainer fell out and I stepped on it. Dr. Schuckart couldn't fix it and it would cost another hundred to replace it. We couldn't afford to buy another.

My teeth moved some. But I can and have lived with them. People have told me I have nice teeth. It sounds good. For a brief time in my life, I could sit in class and run my tongue across my teeth on the back side and they were smooth as piano keys.

Hymns and Wolves

1960's, Smoky Hills

Lunch at our house after church Saturday night.
Finns singing hymns, loud and happy.
Windows open.
Music echoes into the yard on a dark Saturday night.
Kids running around outside, feeling sweaty.
Young guys B.S.ing and smoking cigarettes.

Suloisessa tulevaisuudessa
olemme yhdessä tuolla kauniilla rannalla.
In the sweet by and by, we shall meet on that beautiful shore.
Hallelujah music in one ear,
wolves howling from the hills in the other.

AUTUMN HAS TAKEN

Jacob Wiinamaki

Jacob Wiinamaki was born in Lappajarvi, Finland, and came to America in 1905. He worked in the mines, and the woods while in Negaunee, Michigan. He lived in a boarding house where Hannah Dahl came from Haaparanta, Finland, to work. Jacob kept a diary and wrote several poems expressing his love for Hannah. They married in 1908 and he became a U.S. citizen in 1909. Jacob and Hannah settled on a small homestead along the Popple River near Owen, Wisconsin with their five children. Life was simple, and full of song, games, and several Finnish neighbors. They had a garden, a horse, a sauna, and lots of love. Then the unthinkable happened. Hannah got tuberculosis. After struggling with it for months, she died in 1926. Jacob was heartbroken. After he recorded some poignant writings, he put away his pen. Here is one of his last....

Autumn has taken, has taken
away from here
a small blooming flower,
autumn's rolling waves
swept her away--
autumn has taken my lover.

Oh my cherished, my cherished
  removed from here
  unable to hear
  your lover's voice
  alone I call to her singing--
  only the wind to answer.

Vile Maid of Vellamo
  already has betrothed;
  betrothed my loved one
  alone--
  but not alone oh
  do you know what,
  what it means?

For a remembrance
  not a thing is left me
  only her voice
  an echoing memory
  and a ghostly smile
  upon faded lips.

As a remembrance, a remembrance
  I fasten this wreath
  to your grave, your grave,
  I fasten this salutation
  to the bride of
  the Maid of Vellamo.

Oh the tears, the tears
are flowing
each day I regret,
regret forever that
the one I loved was favored
in Tuonela's darkened river.

Sleep, sleep, sleep
my dearest, my dear one,
my beloved, my friend.
I can do nothing
but lay this wreath,
decorate this--
this grievous grave.

Historical Notes by: Esther Niedzwiecki,
                              daughter of Ella Wiinamaki,
                              daughter of Jacob and Hannah.

Translated by: Daniel Karvonen

Poetic form by: David William Salmela

SNOW WALKER

Snow walker under
a flannel sky

unstuffing itself
with goose's down.

Solitude thick
as a featherbed.

Muffled streets,
breath pulsing

from deep inside
a winter hood.

Hoof-print boots
stamp transient

signs on a shifting
surface drifting

with rifts. Legs
swing at a reindeer

gait, reindeer mitts
direct the flakes.

Only the houses
come alive, their

eyes like windows,
atune to the spell

of a Sami making
the world snow.

Kirsten Dierking

ALL MY RELATIONS

David William Salmela

The great sun
lofted over the broad back of the fairway.
Our green Cushman
tread evenly over rolling grass.
Tools rattled, metal on metal.
Riding with me was my co-worker, Bill.
We rode in silence
squinting into the morning sun.

Bill spat. I drove
He looked at me with dark eyes,
his wild, raven-hair sworn free to the summer
whipped to and fro like
a molting eagle feather working lose.
His eyes did not hide his words.
"If this was fifty years ago and I had a gun,
I'd kill you."
My grey eyes locked deep
with his hate-beaded black ones.
He did not know me.
He saw an enemy.
I saw an ally.

He did not know me.
I reached down inside of my Sami past
where my ancestors were traded
and sold as property
from rich Russian to Swedish Baron--
denied culture, language, our names.

I brought to my face the steely hardness
of inner fortitude.
My straight face bore no emotion
as I peeled the hide from
Reindeer carcass.
My straight face bore no emotion
as my Anishinabe brother murdered me
on the plain of the fourth fairway
that bright summer day.

Let's Think About Good Subjects
for Poems

...said mother
after hearing me
describe my collection of

meat poems
to my sister who had called
and wondered what I'd been up to...

How about Crosswords, or Things
in the China Cabinet?

Jehovah & The Latter Days

I can always tell when
they're coming.

Neighborhood dogs
going nuts. Then they

bang on our door
ask me if I'm concerned

with spiritual things.
Yes, I say, the

neighborhood dogs
are going nuts.

Mary Kinnunen

The International Business Report

Jeff Eaton

From the pages of China Daily,
Finnair's flight attendant
beckons blondly,
sleek as the airline's trim
jets that were the first
over the Wall when Beijing
reopened for business.

Helsinki's consuls and engineers,
shaking hands
for government photographers,
may not know crowds,
but they know how to go
within themselves
as the Chinese do.

And they may not find
a tidy Middle Kingdom
beneath the contracts
and blueprints,
but they'll take care
to lay out the dams, roads,
and forests,
neatly.

For a sauna, they must forget
the misinterpretations
in the tourist hotels, and
get assigned to a friendship
project in Wuhan
or Chongqing,
"Furnaces of the Yangtze."

Then in the sweltering minibus,
they can cover red faces
with two-mao handkerchiefs,
and dream of snow
that falls as abundant
as the cinders and ash
from the mills they pass
on the way to work.

BLOOD RELATIVES

Finnish aunts with hanging bosoms,
square faces and wide arm laps,
said,
"Have something to eat."

Butterscotch pie
chocolate cake
potatoes crisped in lard
raisin filled cookies
sweet biscuit
wild raspberry jam on warm homemade bread
in pools of melted butter,
with egg coffee.

Blood thickened memories.

Judy Harvala Henderson

LEAVING HOME

You come to visit, chase fireflies, play
anti-i-over, and listen to uncles tell stories.

You come for sauna, drink coffee, and listen
to mothers talk of childbirth, Sunday services,
pickle canning, and who's p.g.

You mind children, milk cows, carry wood to
sauna, haul water, chop wood, make hay,
leave for the Cities, Chicago, Duluth.

You learn to type, understand bookkeeping, algebra,
and physics, join the army, work construction,
attend trade school. You teach us how to leave home.

You bring home sweethearts, sit together in church,
hold hands in public, have weddings to dream about,
and babies to baptize.

Finnish cousins,
you come to reunions many years later
and look the same.
Over sips of coffee,
we tell stories,
and we've never left home.

THE SATURDAY AFTERNOON BATH

Julia Klatt Singer

It wasn't more than a minute after my parents drove off down the long, thin dirt driveway, at least a mile long before hitting blacktop, when I stepped in a fresh cow pie twice the size of my shoe, and Simon, my older brother, grabbed hold of the electric fence. Our teenage cousins laughed at us, long-legged boys and girls whose bodies looked more like our parents than ours. A moment later they quieted down and went back to their chores, some of them shaking their heads in disbelief, and muttering, "city folks."

The dairy farm of my aunt Auni and uncle Auno sat in the middle of nowhere, north of Escanaba, west of Lake Michigan, surrounded by rolling hills dotted with stone. This had been copper country, the place to strike it rich a century ago. Delta county. Usually a good place to farm, on the delta, but in the Upper Peninsula nothing seems to do very well for very long. I couldn't have been more than nine or ten on that first visit, old enough for our parents to leave me and Simon alone, with all of them.

A dozen of our relatives lived on this dairy farm. My aunt Auni and uncle Auno, all of their seven children, two of Auno's bachelor brothers and Auni's oldest sister, Aili, a women in her eighties, who still helped with the milking.

They all knew English, but spoke Finnish--a quick, rhythmic language that reminded me of snapping beans. I listened hard, hoping to hear a word I knew, but none emerged from the tangled, clicking sounds.

We were to spend the day on the farm while our parents visited another set of aunts and uncles an hour's drive away. We had only been there a half hour, when lunch was called. It felt like an entire day had already passed, only I wasn't at all hungry.

We sat down at the big oak table in the kitchen, an extra chair and a step-stool squeezed in for Simon and me. We were surrounded by the sound of scraping chairs, loud and gravelly voices, strange words, the smell of coffee percolating, and the rich aroma of meat roasting. A hush passed, and everyone dropped their heads, lowered their eyes, and mumbled a prayer as if they were saying they were sorry for something. No one led, like at church, instead they all began and ended like a soft round. A, Amen, men, A, Amen.

A glass of milk was poured for me, the only thing on the table I could identify besides the bread. I grabbed hold of the large glass, suddenly thirsty, and gulped. It was thick and warm, body temperature. I gagged as I tried not to swallow. "What's wrong with this milk?" I asked. Once again all my cousins laughed.

"That's real milk," my uncle said. "No government involvement there. Real milk, straight from the mother cow."

I felt my cheeks warm, felt I had just done something indecent-- drinking warm, thick milk.

That's all I remember about lunch. The heavy pitcher of warm milk and my glass that wouldn't empty, no matter how hard I tried to swallow it all.

After lunch my uncle took Simon and me out back to help him stoke the sauna. I smelled the burning pine, heard the sap pop in the core of each log, sizzle in the heat. "In a little while," he said, "we take a sauna. It is warm now, no? Later it will be very warm. Make you sweat away the week."

The sauna sat between the house and the dairy barn, a building the size of a one car garage. You entered through a wooden door that led to a narrow hallway that ran the length of the building. It was lined with hooks and a low bench. Three doors, equally spaced, were the only things on the inside wall of the hallway. It was gray inside, sunlight creeping through cracks in the plank boards. This first door led to a room full of split wood. The second door led to the men's sauna, a room made of cedar the size of a large closet. It was even darker inside the sauna, the only source of illumination coming from the fire in the stove. Two benches ran the length of the wall next to, and opposite the door. In the middle of the room sat the wood-burning stove, a round drum with a little square door to put the wood in, and a bin of rocks on the top. A big round black metal pipe went up and out the roof. The third door was the women's sauna. Exactly the same as the men's, except they had the butt end of the stove, and a smaller bin of rocks. It smelled like fire and warm cedar, and felt like my flannel pajamas.

An hour or so later, the sauna bath began. All my cousins were already in. Only my aunts Auni and Aili were still in the kitchen doing the lunch dishes. I lingered at the kitchen table, listening to them chatter, watching the pattern the sun made through the lace curtains dancing in the breeze. Simon had been whisked away minutes ago by our cousin Johnie.

"Come along, Emma," aunt Auni said, "time to go sweat." She took me by the arm and led me and Aili to the sauna. It was darker now inside, I guess because the sun was no longer hidden by clouds, and much much warmer. In the hallway piles of overalls and t-shirts, boots, and wool socks littered the benches and floor.

"Hang your things on that hook," my aunt Aili said, "then come on in." I turned toward the wall and took off my tennis shoes, tucked a sock in the toes of each one, and carefully hung my shirt and shorts on the hook.

Aunt Auni's head popped out of the sauna door and said, "Underwear comes off too, sweety." As the door banged shut I heard her say, "and not a peep out of one of you." Soft giggles mingled with the popping wood.

The first sensation was heat. A thick air too heavy to breath, too hot to swallow. Then flesh. I had never seen a naked body but my own, never seen my mother in less than her slip, my dad in less that his undershorts and white t-shirt. Even my brother's body was a mystery to me. We bathed together until only a few years ago, but he always wrapped a washcloth around his penis like a loin cloth, and made me close my eyes when he got out. I never thought of peeking. What was there to see? I didn't have anything interesting to look at.

I glanced around trying to find a place to sit, a place to hold my eyes. The fire flickered through the cracks in the pipe, creating flashes of light on my aunts and cousins bodies. Big round breasts hung and swayed with ruby and mauve nipples staring right at me. All the women sat talking, legs crossed, as if they were having tea. Nobody's body looked like mine, small and flat, lacking description. Their laps were dark and hidden behind small, firm bellies.

I climbed up on the bench and tried to disappear. I felt little and white, my nipples flat and pink. I crossed my legs and closed my eyes and couldn't get the picture of all that flesh surrounding me out of my mind. I didn't want to open my eyes and see it all again, but something about their voices made me want to look. They were all naked, with womanly bodies, sweating, yet acting like nothing was strange. It was like the milk, both familiar and yet somehow risque.

I remember the heat entering my skin and my lungs and eventually feeling like I was part of it all, merging into the wood bench, their unfamiliar words and the heat of the fire.

"Time to cool off," my cousin Janice said. She was sixteen and curvy without being fat. "Follow me." She climbed down the bench and led me to the door. I watched as her hips tilted, her butt bouncing up and down with each stride. We entered the hallway and then opened the door to the outside. Light flooded my eyes and I remember blinking hard once or twice before I figured out what was happening. As we stepped into the bright yard, someone said, "ready" and Janice laughed yes and a bucket of cold water coated our bodies. I opened my eyes and saw most of the men and some of the women all standing around the yard, naked, dripping and chatting like they were at a church picnic. Aili came out of the house with an arm load of towels and began handing them out. I tried not to look at the men, especially my uncles, with their dark hair and round cylinders of flesh hanging between their legs. I tried not to see them at all, but it was hard. It was broad daylight and the backyard was full of naked people.

I spotted Simon across the yard, running around with Johnie and a bucket of water. Simon was still wearing his white briefs with the blue waistband. Some of the cousins went back to the sauna for another sweat, some to the house to get dressed for the evening; it was Saturday after all. I stood there naked and warm, white and creamy like the milk, feeling the sun's rays on my chest, watching the light breeze rustle the small blond hairs on my arm, with nothing, absolutely nothing, to hide.

BERRY PICKING

David William Salmela

At twenty-three I thought I cut a pretty cool picture as I turned my motorcycle on the half-mile dirt road to my Gramma's and Hugo B.'s farm. My motorcycle spun a web of dust in the glimmering summer sunshine. The sun dazzled from my gas tank. Gramma and Hugo B. didn't know I was coming. I reached the house just as Gramma came out to see who it was. She waved to me.

"Päivää." I shouted.

"Well, hello," said Gramma.

"Kuinka se menee?"

"We're doing fine. Come in."

I took off my helmet, hugged Gramma and went in.

"Was it a long ride?" my Grandmother asked in English. I would try to talk Finnish to her, but she always answered in English. I gave up on Finnish, "Pretty long."

I looked in the other room. My grandpa, Hugo B., didn't look up from his paper. He had his reading glasses perched on his sharp nose and a cigar in his teeth. I decided not to say hello to him, either. I visited with Gramma instead.

"What's new around here?"

"Oh, well, you now Mrs. Aho..."

"Mm, hmm," I affirmed, even though I didn't know her.

"...she and her sister went out berry picking, but there aren't many on account of all the rain."

I sipped my coffee as I listened. "Hey, Gramma, do you know where the cranberry bog is my mom talks about?"

"No. You'd have to ask Hugo B. We used to get lots of

cranberries from there. We'd sell them in town."

"I was hoping someone would take me there, or maybe just go out and look around for some blueberries."

I heard a noise. I looked up. Hugo B. stood in the doorway. He had his cane and a plastic bucket in one hand and another pail in the other hand. "Come," he said.

I gulped the last of my coffee. I kissed Gramma. "See you later."

"You better take some bug dope."

"Okay."

The two of us went out. Hugo B. stood next to the motorcycle. "Let's go," he said.

I looked at him carefully. I didn't think he would be able to get on what with his bad hip and knees. Then I looked at his jaw, it was set firm. "I'll move the bike over to the stoop, Hugo B., then you get on."

He swung his leg, but not high enough. I held the heavy motorcycle so it wouldn't tip. I reached out to balance him so he wouldn't tip. He straightened and tried again.

"You made it," I congratulated.

"Go," he replied.

I felt scared. If we fell, it would all be over. I'd never get him home. I shifted into first and took off. Hugo B. held the pails one in each hand. I noticed he'd left the cane behind.

We wound through the backwoods' back road. When we reached the township road he said, "Oikealle."

I turned right. The foundation of the one-room schoolhouse my mother attended until third grade slid behind us. Soon we reached the blacktop.

"Vasemmalle," he said. I turned left. The asphalt whined.

"Stop! Turn here." I turned in on an old logging road. We didn't talk much. I concentrated on not tipping over. The road got narrower and more rutted. Every once in awhile we turned. By now we were deep in the woods. We motored in and out of patches of sunlight.

"Stop." I applied the brakes. I set my foot down firmly to hold up the heavy machine. Ahead of us the road continued on. To our right was a steep embankment. A narrow trail led up the hill and disappeared over the crest. It looked more like a washout than a trail.

"Up there," he said.

"But Hugo B., this isn't a dirt bike. If we fall, we'll get hurt, besides, I'm not that good of a driver."

"HEP!" he shouted.

"But..."

"HEP!!!" I gunned it. The back tire skewed dangerously. Sand and gravel shot into the trees behind us. The plastic pails clanked noisily on the sides of the cycle. Time seemed suspended. The front tire lifted over the ridge of the hill. For eons we were poised, rearing in the air and then we landed. We made it!

The trail widened and became a normal two-tracked logging road. The road gently descended down a long incline. On either side of us were deep ravines. There were huge bogs at the bottom of the valleys between the hills. In these bogs were high bush cranberries.

"I hauled many gunny sacks fulls out of here," Hugo B. said as we drove past. We did not stop. We drove on, descending the ridge steadily.

We rounded a corner in the road. I stopped quickly, almost upsetting us. We had come to the flood plain of the Shell River. The water was gushing across the logging road. I eyed it speculatively.

I eased the bike up to the edge of the river. The current looked strong enough to sweep us off the motorcycle. Water lapped at the bottom of the front tire. I could not see the depth of the water over the road because of the sun's glare.

"Hugo B., I don't think we can make it. It's totally flooded over the..."

"HEP!"

"But we'll be washed away!"

"HEP ! ! !"

That 'HEP' made me nervous. It was the same tone of voice he used when he first told me never to call him Grandpa. His name was Hugo B. and don't you ever forget it. I goosed it. We did a little wheelie before I got the bike under control. We leaped into the water like some sort of mutant deer gleaming metallic blue. The water splashed up around us, glittering diamonds in the forest green.

I could only guess where the road was. We splashed forward, a giant two-headed salmon forging upstream. Suddenly, we were on dry land. My feet were soaked, but we were upright and tooling along.

I couldn't see Hugo B., but I could feel him grinning behind me.

We reached some blacktop far on the other side of the farm. I gave it gas, throttled up. I felt his grin grow larger. Our eyes squinted partially closed against the late afternoon sun. We leaned into the curves toward home, plastic ice cream pails catching berries of wind.

I thought we cut a pretty cool picture flying down the highway-- a grandson and Hugo B.

Katrine Keranen

o finland

o finland
i consumed your macaroni hot dish faithfully
seasoned with your runny ketchup twice
a week finland your storebought macaroni box
made its aluminum presence known in that oven
i never quite understood with those
strange pictograms and that extra dial
o finland my plates were second hand
junk not even arabia keramikka o finland
your coffee cups were too damn small
finland and whats up with those exercise
suits finland where i spent those grey
days by your harbors your dirty industrial
docks inland i sucked off your healthcare teat
spent long hours in your identical waiting rooms
those tables and shelves of the finest laminate
design so functional so equal so finland i
got lost trying to find addresses in your
housing compounds fields full of buildings
all the same full of apartments all the same
full of rooms all the same oh finland
where were the kantele playing fisherman
in wooden rowboats where were the blueberry
stained maidens where were the architects
and designers finland i was promised salmon
pie you gave me pea soup in a can

Will Lahti

AFTERWORD

We are looking for submissions of stories, poetry, and illustrations for future publications from OTSA PRESS. Please contact us, David William Salmela or Judy Harvala Henderson at:

OTSA PRESS
5871 Covington Lane
Minnetonka MN 55345-6216
(612) 934-9682
e-mail: dwsalmela@aol.com

ACKNOWLEDGEMENTS:

Julia K. Singer: "The Saturday Afternoon Bath" previously published by Rag Mag, a journal of writing, 1996.

Sheila J. Packa: "The Cure" is an excerpt from an autobiographical novel in progress called Over the Divide.

Kirsten Dierking: "Snow Walker" previously published in Mother Superior, a journal distributed in Grand Marais, MN under the title "Walk to Work in December."

Judy Henderson: "Blood Relatives" previously published in The Metropolitan, the student newspaper of Metropolitan State University, St. Paul, MN, April, 1997.

David W. Salmela: "Berry Picking" previously published in The Finnish American Reporter from "Salmela's World" column, Nov. 1993.

Mary Kinnunen: "Homespun Barbie", originally written for Mondo Barbie Redux, St. Martin's Press, 1994. "Let's Think About Good Subjects for Poems" and "Jehovah & The Latter Days" first appeared in North Coast Review, 1997.

All previously published stories and poems reprinted by permission of the authors.